Fred Martin

e-geography

Using ICT i… …graphy

Geographical Association

acknowledgements

The author and publishers are grateful to the following people and organisations for permission to include copyright material in this book:

The Advisory Unit; Bluesky International Ltd; Peter H Dana; DfES; Digital Worlds; ESRI (UK); Eurostat; Gemtree; Getmapping plc; Geomantics; Geopacks; The Globe Program; Greenpeace; Half-Baked Software; Hardenhuish High School; Hugh Mothersole; InfoMapper; Istituto Nazionale di Statistica; Alan L Jones; Bob Jones; The Met Office; MindJet; The *Mirror*; Multimap; NESTA Futurelab; The Ordnance Survey; QCA Innovating with Geography; RM plc; Selwyn Electronics; Staffordshire Learning Net; University of Hull Geography Department; US Census; World Climate; Matthew Zook.

Whilst we have made every effort to trace the owners of all copyright material, we have not been able to do so in every case. We apologise, therefore, if we have inadvertently infringed copyright and will endeavour to rectify this at reprint.

ISBN 1 84377 170 5
First published 2006
Impression number 10 9 8 7 6 5 4 3 2 1
Year 2009 2008 2007 2006

Published by the Geographical Association, 160 Solly Street, Sheffield S1 4BF.
Website: www.geography.org.uk
E-mail: ga@geography.org.uk
The Geographical Association is a registered charity: no 313129.

The Publications Officer of the GA would be happy to hear from other potential authors who have ideas for geography books. You may contact the Officer via the GA at the address above.

Edited by Andrew Shackleton, Asgard Publishing Services
Designed by Bryan Ledgard
Printed and bound in China through Colorcraft Ltd, Hong Kong

Fred Martin

e-geography

Using ICT in quality geography

Geographical Association

foreword

Globally connected electronic media are part of our daily lives, and twenty-first century geographical education must engage with the twenty-first century geography of people's lives. We interact with the wider world predominantly via electronic communication and information. Via the internet, everyone can access a massive geographical database. The challenge for us as geography teachers (and a big responsibility it is) is to help our students use this communication and information in a constructive way.

These learners of twenty-first century ***e-geography*** need a critical eye, an eye for fact and opinion, an eye for quality. How does the virtual flow of information affect people's lives? Who does it exclude? Whose pattern of interaction is global, and whose is not? Our responsibility is to help students acquire the techniques to question and critically evaluate; to gain a perception of places; and to understand partial truths, in a way that gives them tools to make sense of that uncertain knowledge.

At the heart of ***e-geography*** is pedagogical thinking, literally the way ICT can be used to help students learn more effectively. The proposition is that it's not worth using ICT in geography unless it adds value, and this is the focus of the series of illustrative examples in this resource. If you need ideas for how ICT can help students achieve higher standards in geography, then this book and CD will help enormously. For just two of many practical examples, 'Working with words' tackles the vital skills of relating words to images and images to words, helping students to better communicate their geographical understanding and 'The spatial dimension' will enable you to help visual learners manipulate pictures and maps.

Fred Martin is one of those rare educators who is on one level theoretical and challenging but on another also practical and classroom-oriented. ***e-geography*** has all the elements of both. This book is full of practical ideas, but they are grounded in a clear philosophical framework of curiosity about the world which, harnessed to purposeful enquiry and the intelligent use of ICT, will enable students to make more rapid progress in their geographical understanding.

Chris Durbin, Hong Kong, December 2005

Chris Durbin is Secondary Education Adviser for the English Schools Foundation in Hong Kong and formerly Inspector for Geography for Staffordshire Education Service, the founder of www.sln.org.uk/geography and Education Adviser for BBC Education.

contents

Using this resource

The resource package

The focus of the resource

The overall focus of this resource is on the *quality* of geographical education, together with an exploration of ways in which the use of ICT can help to improve the quality of geography. Although the focus is on quality, this is of course inseparable from how the subject is taught and learnt. Even the distinction between teaching and learning becomes blurred, given that teaching is more effective when the teacher models the learning process for the students, and that the students themselves can learn by presenting and communicating their work to others, often by using ICT.

The scope of the resource

The scope of the resource is broad but, given the rapidly expanding field of ICT, it would be foolish to attempt to be comprehensive. Although some aspects of geographical education and ICT applications are dealt with in some detail, others are only mentioned briefly. One aim is to present ideas that are realistic and based on present practice, at least in some schools. Another aim is to help teachers of geography, not only to develop their own vision of how ICT can be used in their lessons, but also to think about some more fundamental questions about where the use of ICT could be taking the subject.

The book and the CD

To help achieve these aims, the resource consists of both a book and a CD-Rom. This combination is needed to take advantage of what each format can do best, while at the same time ensuring that they complement one another. In short, the book provides the key ideas about how ICT can both raise and, in some cases, define standards of high-quality work in the subject. The CD mainly provides samples of work in geography that have been created by using different ICT applications.

The rationale of the chapters

This book is organised into chapters that reflect how ICT can be used in the different types of activities and skills that are relevant to work in geography. The CD-Rom is organised in the same way so that the two can be closely related.

Enquiry is a central activity and skill in geography. However, since it involves all of the other skills and activities, it is a theme that is incorporated in the different chapters, rather than forming a separate section on its own. In a similar way, the use of thinking skills in geography plays a part in every aspect of the work, so these too are included throughout the chapters.

One effect of this structure is that the same ICT applications can appear in several chapters. For example, drawing programs can be used in a variety of ways, such as in mapping, understanding processes and using photos. The rationale for this approach is to ensure that the focus is on how the geography can be enhanced by the use of ICT and not the other way round.

The book

Each chapter in the book begins with a set of questions that the chapter aims to answer. The content of the chapters is then divided into a standard format consisting of four main parts (except in the first and final chapters, which have their own unique structures). Key ideas relating to the use of ICT in geography are explored in the following sections (titles are adapted for each chapter):

- **Focus.** The focus and its context for the chapter.
- **Defining standards.** High standards in geography are defined in a way that goes beyond the definitions provided in the NC Orders for Geography and exam board course documents. Without a clear understanding of what constitutes high quality in the subject, the debate over using ICT or any other methods to raise standards is largely futile.
- **Using ICT.** The different roles which ICT can play in the teaching and learning of the types of work in geography that form the focus for each chapter, and how high-quality geography can be achieved by using ICT.
- **Wider issues.** Ideas relating to the pedagogy of using ICT, and issues about some of the effects that ICT may have on the content, concepts, teaching and learning strategies, standards and how they can be assessed.

Additional items

Items additional to the main text are mostly presented in special panels so that the key ideas can be both exemplified and related to other aspects of the curriculum:

- **ICT applications.** A list at the start of each chapter gives the main ICT applications relevant to the chapter.
- **Making links.** These panels aim to show where there are links between ICT in geography and key documents such as the NC Orders for Geography, the NC Orders for ICT, Thinking Skills and various KS3 (Secondary) Strategy strands. Although many of the references apply to

work at KS3, there is no intention that the ideas in the book should be confined to that level.

- **Check it out.** These comments invite teachers to reflect on some ideas in the light of their own experience and practice. Some of them could form the basis for departmental INSET work.
- **Teaching ideas.** Ideas that could form the basis of lessons that make use of ICT with students. The aim is not to provide 'off the shelf' lessons, but to provide a skeleton of ideas that can be adapted for use with students of different ages and abilities.
- **Technique tips.** While the book does not aim to be a user's manual for different ICT applications, some basic guidance is included on how to use a selected range of tools and functions. This usually relates to the use of standard Office and other generic software.
- **Illustrations.** Those in the book, together with their captions, aim to provide some visual prompts to accompany the text. Further illustrations are included as samples on the CD-Rom. Often the illustration says more than the text about how effective ICT can be.
- **Websites.** The names of websites are included in the book, though these are not accompanied by their web addresses (URLs). All the web addresses, however, can be accessed from the CD-Rom via a link to the Geographical Association's website. This will allow them to be updated as necessary.

The CD-Rom

No resource on the use of ICT could be complete without either an accompanying CD-Rom or a website. This is a case of when the medium and the message need to be linked.

The origin of the samples

The CD-Rom provides samples of work created by teachers and others, mostly for classroom use, though some have been written mainly to demonstrate how an ICT technique can be used in geography. As such, they are written in individual styles and vary from the basic to the more complex. They are not intended to provide definitive examples of ICT-generated work, or to be used without modification. A limiting factor on the inclusion of samples has been the fact that teachers can now make extensive use of maps and other digital resources in ways that do not infringe copyright laws when used in school, but that do infringe these laws in a book (which counts as commercial use). This is also why some of the original samples had to be modified, sometimes compromising their original quality.

Access to software

Most of the samples were written using generic software such as MS Word, MS Excel and drawing programs such as MS Paint. Some, however, were written using software that a school may not have, such as interactive whiteboard software. These are intended to be illustrative rather than actually to recommend the software. Although this may be frustrating for teachers who do not have the software, it would have been an omission not to have included as wide a range of items as possible.

Further samples

There is, of course, no shortage of good resources that have been created using ICT. These are available on websites and on other CD-Roms. Links to some of the websites are provided, though there is so much material available that only a fraction can be mentioned. Teachers are urged to play their own part in building up this bank of shared resources, no matter what they feel about the quality of their own work. Good ideas are always worth sharing with others, and thanks to the development of ICT, there have never been so many ways to share and learn from one another.

Chapter 1 The digital dimension

Key questions

- In what ways do students use and have access to ICT?
- How are digital resources integrated through ICT applications and hardware?
- How can ICT help both to define and to raise standards in geography?
- What is the educational rationale for using ICT in teaching and learning?
- How can teaching and learning in geography and ICT be complementary?
- How can geographers create a case for greater access to ICT resources?

Focus on the students

Today's children in the UK are wired into a multi-media world. This may not be true for all of them, but it is certainly true for many. More than half of today's school students have access to a computer in their home and, of course, work with computers is compulsory as part of their education. Although the ability to read text is still essential, their everyday experiences are as much to do with watching and listening as with reading. Words are often replaced by

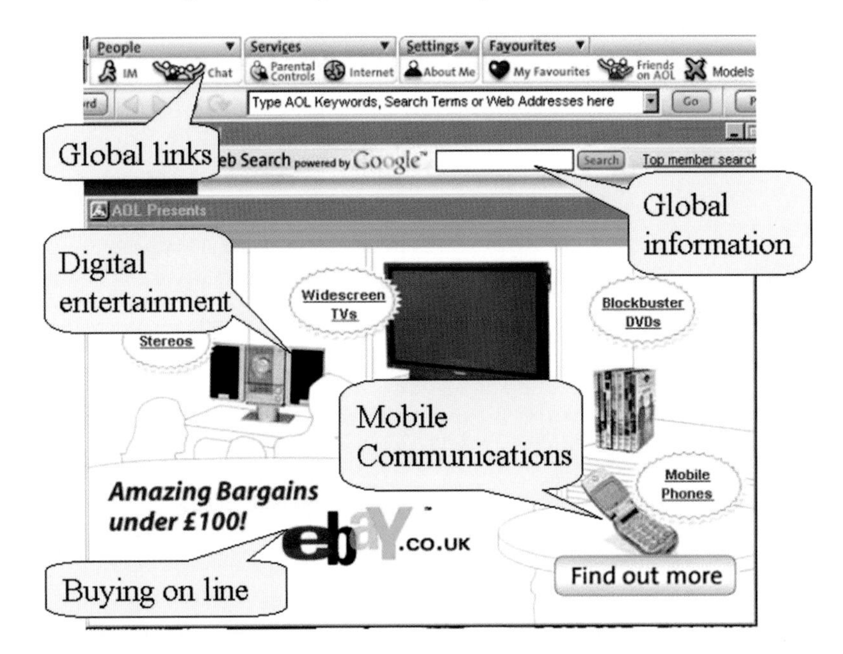

Figure 1.1 *Today's children are using digital technologies for every form of communication.*

symbols and icons. Look at any computer desktop screen to see the truth of this. Even music is sold as much by the video as by the sound. Children have become accustomed to being entertained by multi-media resources. One result of this emphasis on sound and vision is that there appears to be neither the time or the demand for quiet reflective reading. This is an oversimplified description of the situation, but teachers must nonetheless reckon with it.

It is tempting to engage in a pedagogic debate as to whether there should be a distinct separation between entertainment and education. For the children, however, it is a debate that lacks meaning. Teachers must live with the fact that competing for their students' attention is becoming more difficult, and that for most children the novelty value of ICT has now largely subsided. Generating motivation and interest by using ICT can no longer be guaranteed. But because more students have the technical competence to use ICT, the challenge now is to use this to the advantage of teaching and learning. It is also important to consider how the use of ICT may more fundamentally affect not only how teaching and learning are done, but also what is to be taught and learnt.

The reality, fortunately, is that there is no longer a stark division between text, visual images and sound. The term multi-media has been created to recognise how all three can be integrated. It is also the case that, despite warnings of the demise of reading, more books are now being published and read than ever before. It is still possible for a children's book to become a best-seller, though it is seldom long before a film of the book is made; the DVD usually follows shortly. Some books are even written with the aim of making them into films, while the reverse process is also not unusual. There are many TV series that are also sold as books. Many of these have non-fiction content, often described as history or nature, though seldom labelled geography.

Check it out

Think about the students that you teach:

- How many of them have access to a PC at home?
- How many own their own PC?
- How many have internet access?
- What software do they have on their computers at home?

If you know the answers to these questions, do you have strategies for taking advantage of this information?

Making links

Key Stage 3 National Strategy
Literacy and learning in geography

Because of advances in technology, today's pupils have greater access to more text in more forms than ever before. Moreover, recent international surveys have shown English pupils to be amongst the best readers in the world. Yet, paradoxically, teachers' expectations of the extent to which pupils can learn from text are sometimes low.

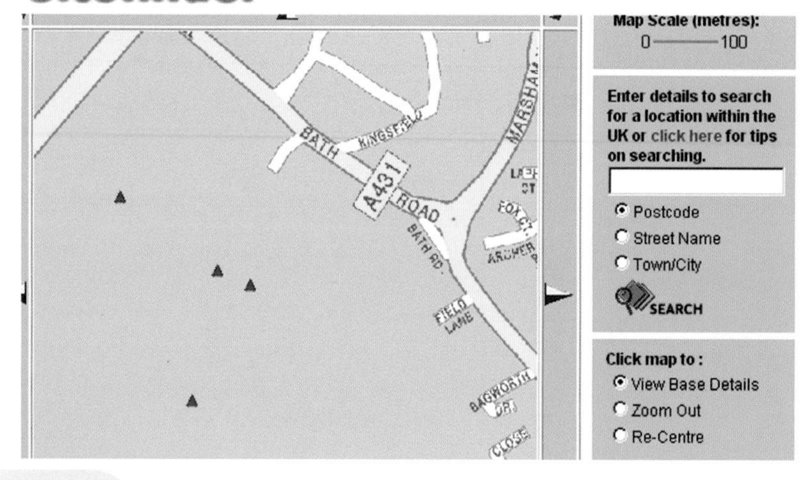

Name of Operator	Orange
Operator Site Ref.	AVN0077
Height of Antenna	14 Metres
Frequency Range	1800 MHz
Transmitter Power	26.9 dBW
Maximum licensed power	32 dBW
Type of Transmission	GSM

Figure 1.2 *Different forms of ICT are creating a new landscape that has effects on people and the environment.*

The first thing teachers must recognise is that the use of multi-media in education is here to stay – this is in spite of whatever one might think about the importance of text relative to other forms of communication, or whether entertainment and education should occupy separate worlds. This applies not only to geography, but to every other subject. This situation, however, is one to be positively embraced. There are certainly some problems in too great a retreat from the use of text, but for developing an understanding and raising standards in geography, a multi-media approach has the potential to bring more benefits than problems.

Engaging students

One of the keys to successful teaching and learning is making sure that the students are engaged. It is, for example, more likely that students will be engaged with the work if the ideas and topics are presented to them in ways that are both visually and intellectually stimulating. They are also more likely to be engaged if the activities they do are interactive and they have some degree of ownership over them.

Make it live

A lesson can be engaging it is presented in ways that use strategies and techniques that go beyond the stimulation achieved by using no more than a textbook and an overhead or 35-mm slide projector. Places can be brought alive by the use of sound with high-quality images on a big screen. Moving images through animation and video can be used to illustrate and explain processes. ICT can do both of these things, and can do them well. The smells and tactile experiences of places would be other dimensions to bring into the classroom. Although the technology exists to do these things, they are difficult to replicate in a classroom – but perhaps it is just a matter of time.

Digital interfaces

The technology for presenting subject material has developed rapidly over the last 30 years. Almost every type of resource is now available in digital form. The different technologies and hardware have developed interfaces that allow digital resources to be moved almost seamlessly between them, changing from one medium to another. They are said to be interoperable. There are some problems with incompatible file formats, but there is usually a way to resolve these. Using ICT in this way not only keeps the students' attention, but can also play a part in developing their understanding and in making the learning process more engaging and enjoyable.

Developing motivation

The motivation to learn can also come from the ways in which students become engaged with the material they are studying. The use of ICT can help with this, whether it be a CD-Rom, an interactive website or an on-screen resource created with generic software. Students can be motivated to learn by being able to take decisions while running a simulation or, as they may call it, a game. This could, for example, be a simulation to show how their decisions affect profits on a farm or how a coastline could be protected.

The use of an interactive whiteboard is another way to achieve engagement and motivation. During a presentation on an interactive whiteboard, students can be encouraged to come to the front and add their own thoughts to photos, or to engage in more active techniques that involve moving text and images on the screen. There is something almost magical about how they work. Perhaps it is partly to do with the power that students feel when technology responds instantly to the pen they are using, or even when they touch the screen with their finger. Perhaps the reasons don't matter as long as the result is effective.

At this point, it is worth explaining that, although interactive whiteboards are being bought in rapidly increasing numbers, no separate section of this book has been devoted to their use. This is because, although they have considerable scope for making the teaching and learning more effective, they do not affect the content and the quality of the geography in any way that cannot be achieved by using other technologies, whether hardware or software. For example, drag-and-drop activities carried out by a student in front of the whole class can help develop engagement and motivation. While this is beneficial to the teaching and learning, the geography itself is not improved, and the activity could of course be organised in another way. An interactive whiteboard when used with its software is certainly a useful tool for integrating text, photos, diagrams, animations and other resources. This is certainly valuable for the teaching and learning, but is not the main focus for this book.

Check it out

Find out about the different types of interactive whiteboard from the company websites. Look at samples of what interactive whiteboard software will enable you to do. In particular, focus on the interactive tools and functions, rather than simply using it as a projector screen.

Websites

Promethean
Smart Technologies
cardiffschools.net

Choice and research

There is likely to be greater engagement and motivation when students are allowed to choose and to make individual discoveries – for example, to choose a topic or place in which they have an interest. They are likely to find out information that even the teacher may not have already found. They are also likely to be led, often by accident, to other topics that might deepen their interest even further. It is tempting to feel that learning needs to be focused and controlled in order to avoid accidental learning. This approach, however, can kill off the joy of discovery by denying students the opportunity to make their own connections between processes, some of which may be outside academic subject boundaries. There is always an element of interest in exploring places that were previously unknown, whether such 'places' are on the ground or in the mind.

New topics in geography

ICT is more than just a tool. For many people, it is a way of life that brings its own geographical effects. At one level, it is an industry that creates jobs with effects on the landscape and environment. It also affects the location of these industries. Communications through the use of ICT gives flows of data and information around the world, setting up a modern counterpart to shipping and air routes. It is an industry that operates not only on land but also in space and on other planets. For geography, ICT has the potential to open up new topics, places and dimensions to study that are likely to be relevant to the students' own lives, both now and in the future. They need to find out about what is happening now, rather than always looking back to what has happened in the past. Using ICT to study the geography of ICT seems to have potential for new and exciting dimensions in the subject. Thinking about where these developments may go has the potential to capture the students' imagination, as well as leading them to acquire new knowledge and understanding.

Building on success

Most teachers at some time have to battle against the students' claim that they can't draw a map, for example. This is especially true for students whose natural graphic skills, and often also their lack of proper map-drawing equipment, mean that their efforts too often end in frustration and failure. There can be a similar problem during activities in which calculations are involved – for example, in running a simulation. While failure brings about lack of motivation, success can have the opposite and desired effect. The use of ICT in some aspects of geography can help to overcome at least some of these problems. ICT can also allow students to focus on the geographical ideas, without their time and energies becoming diverted.

Teaching idea

The students can list the different aspects of ICT that they use during a typical day. For each aspect, they should ask the following questions:

- How does it affect what you do?
- What kinds of jobs does it create?
- Where has it been made?
- Does it have any direct effect on the environment?
- Does it change the landscape in any way, directly or indirectly?
- How might some of these technologies might develop further in the future?

Websites

The Geography of Cyberspace Directory

Zooknic Internet Intelligence

Maps showing the numbers of internet users

Check it out

Research into the motivational effect of ICT on students carried out by Lancaster University (March 2004) yielded the results below. Think about these results in the light of your own experiences.

- While ICT motivates both boys and girls, it probably has a greater effect on boys, helping them to stay more focused on their work for longer.
- ICT helps secondary pupils take pride in their work, is helpful for coursework and supports research work.
- Behaviour in lessons is better in most cases and tasks are completed on time when ICT is used.
- Pupils gain confidence because they can do things that they have not been able to do before, they can explore more and they can share ideas with others.
- The use of interactive whiteboards increases the pace and effectiveness of lessons and is extremely effective in motivating pupils to learn.

Does the research have any implications for the way you use ICT in your teaching?

Website

BECTA

Making links

Key Stage 3 National Strategy
ICT across the curriculum: ICT in geography

ICT as a teaching tool

So far we have reviewed the use of ICT as a learning tool for pupils and have acknowledged how pupils who are confident and proficient in ICT can bring with them opportunities for extending their learning as they use their ICT in other subjects in the school curriculum.

However, existing and emerging ICT teaching tools provide further opportunities to enhance subjects and add value to teaching and learning. For example, the use of interactive whiteboards, video projection units, microscopes connected to computers, prepared spreadsheets to capture and model data, CD-Roms, presentations with video and carefully selected resources from the internet all provide examples of how ICT can be embedded into subject teaching.

Figure 1.3 *Flows of communications on the internet create new patterns of communication (from the Geography of Cyberspace Directory). © Brian Reid*

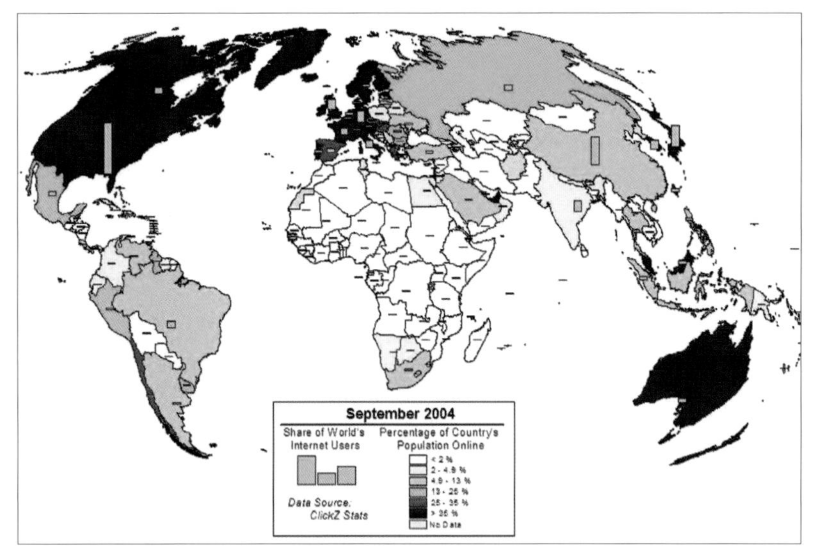

Figure 1.4 *The internet is a fast-growing global phenomenon with implications for the geography of people (from Zooknic Internet Intelligence).© Matthew Zook*

Geography is a subject that has the potential to be taught and learned in ways that are both enjoyable and effective. But if taught dryly, the topics and ideas can be deemed remote and therefore irrelevant. ICT is not the solution to every problem, but when used to its full potential by an enthusiastic and knowledgeable teacher, it can undoubtedly bring enormous benefits in motivation, interest and quality of learning.

Making links

QCA Schemes of Work

The use of ICT can enhance learning in geography by:

- providing a range of information sources to enhance geographical understanding
- supporting the development of a body of geographical knowledge
- providing images of people, places and environments
- enabling pupils to communicate and exchange information with people in other places
- contributing to pupils' awareness of the impact of information systems (e.g. GIS) on the changing world.

Making links

BECTA: Geography

Pupils' entitlement to ICT

Pupils studying geography are entitled to use ICT:

- to enhance their skills of geographical enquiry
- to gain access to a wide range of geographical knowledge and information sources
- to deepen their understanding of environmental and spatial relationships
- to experience alternative images of people, place and environment
- to consider the wider impact of ICT on people, place and environment.

Website

BECTA: Geography

Making links

Edexcel GCSE Syllabus A (illustrative GCSE syllabus)

Information and Communications Technology

The GCSE criteria require that students make effective use of ICT in ways appropriate to the subject. ICT should be built into any teaching programme developed from the specification, and the use of ICT is formally assessed in the coursework.

Appropriate uses of ICT in geography would include the use of data loggers to capture primary data; the use of the internet and CD-Roms to research information; the use of databases and spreadsheets to present and manipulate the information; and the use of word processing or desktop publishing packages and graphics packages to write up coursework investigations.

Check it out

Read these statements about the relationship between ICT and geography from the QCA's *Innovating with Geography* website:

- The use of ICT can enhance teaching and learning of geography. It also contributes to the development of pupils' ICT skills.
- Children can use ICT to:
  - support investigations and enquiry
  - communicate and present ideas in different ways
  - access different sources of information to enhance their geographical knowledge
  - recognise patterns and relationships using different databases and spreadsheets and multi-media
  - understand how ICT influences communication, leisure and the world of work.

How closely do these statements match your use of ICT in geography?

Website

QCA: Innovating with Geography

ICT to raise standards

Can ICT can play any significant part in raising standards in geography? This is a question over which much time, effort and money has already been spent. Behind the question, there is the logical implication that if it does not raise standards, then it should not be used. If, however, it does help to raise standards, then teachers and students should use it more often.

It is usually difficult to identify any single cause of a change in general educational standards or in the standards in one particular subject. There is even no real agreement as to whether standards in general have gone up or down, in spite of apparent evidence from the seemingly ever-upward trend of examination results. Higher results are met with scepticism, the suspicion being that the standards expected have been progressively lowered. This is not the place in which to explore these arguments. It is, however, pertinent to consider how the use of ICT can impact on the content and quality of the geography that is taught and learned.

Work that looks better

There can be no doubt that the use of ICT can have effects on some aspects of the quality of work in geography. It can, for example, help to improve the appearance of a student's work. Written work looks neater and is more likely to be spelt correctly. Maps and graphs can be produced to a higher standard of technical proficiency. Neatness, however, is not a valid criterion against which to assess the quality of most types of work in geography. An exception is in graphics work, whether maps, diagrams or graphs, where technical proficiency and the professional quality that it produces should be part of the assessment criteria. Neatness may also play a part in ensuring that students have a clear record of their work so that they can review it and revise from it. This will be important for as long as passing tests and achieving good marks in public examinations are regarded as criteria that define achievement.

Thinking with ICT

It would be hard to argue that ICT can directly affect the quality of geographical description, analysis, interpretation or application, i.e. those aspects that belong to the cognitive domain. This aspect of the work forms part of developing what is now generally known as *thinking skills*. There are some arguments that the use of ICT can have an indirect effect on the quality of thought, for example, by providing easy access to more and varied data and information. It also enables students to edit text until it demonstrates their understanding better. This is a way in which the computer can be used as a 'mind tool'. From a teaching perspective, it can be argued that the effective use of digital multi-media can enable a teacher to better explain processes so that students can understand them more quickly and comprehensively. It can also be used to give students opportunities to engage directly with the material through simulations and other interactive techniques. The combination of computer, data projector and interactive whiteboard has become a powerful tool for bringing about what is little short of a revolution in the classroom, or at least in some classrooms.

Ways in which thinking skills in geography can be developed through the use of ICT are explored throughout this book. Conversely, ICT skills can be developed through activities designed to develop thinking skills. However, the emphasis in this book is on identifying and developing quality in the geography, not in ICT. It is certainly useful if students are able to learn new ICT skills or apply existing ICT skills through their work in geography. The more important question is whether the ICT skills have done anything to produce a better quality of geography.

Making links

NC Orders, DfEE

Thinking skills
- information processing
- reasoning
- enquiry
- creative thinking
- evaluation.

Websites
Thinking Skills Research Centre
Mind Friendly Learning
Thinking through Geography
Buzzin
Thinking skills in geography
teachernet
Higher-order thinking skills

Defining quality in geography

There comes a point at which the argument over the relationship between ICT and standards becomes futile. Any definition of standards depends on the criteria that are used to define the standards. The present position is generally one in which ICT is being used in order to meet standards that are defined against criteria that are themselves poorly defined and that give little weight to what ICT can do well. The standards against which achievement is defined in geography at key stages 1, 2 and 3 are set out in the Level Descriptions (Attainment Targets) in the National Curriculum Orders for Geography. At best, these are imprecise tools for making judgements about standards. To be fair, they were never intended to be anything other than broad-brush statements for use at the end of each key stage to give a general indication of the level at which a student was working. At GCSE and AS/A2 level, standards are defined against marking criteria, often with further exemplification in the form of grade descriptors. These too are imprecise tools, though they appear to satisfy their current purpose. There are few specific references either to the use of ICT or, more importantly, to what ICT can do well, either in the NC Orders for Geography or in the Exam Board marking criteria at any level.

Giving credit to ICT

So although geography teachers may have their own ideas about what constitutes good-quality geography, it is difficult to give credit to anything that is not defined in the 'official' definitions of standards. As a simple example, although it may be better geography to draw a map using GIS software than to use hand-drawn methods, there is nothing in the present assessment criteria that can give additional credit for doing it in this way. This situation means, that in many aspects of geography, students can achieve the same standards by using traditional methods as by using ICT. This is mainly because there is no credit given to the additional quality that the use of ICT can bring. It can even seem as if progression in graphic work ends at key stage 3. So although the technology exists to do many things better, this is not reflected in the criteria that define achievement.

The question of standards is a complex one that is developed further throughout this book. In each chapter, space is devoted to exploring what it means to define high quality in the different aspects of work in geography – for example, in drawing maps, writing geographical text, using photos and understanding processes. These definitions are intended to go beyond the present limited and poorly understood criteria that define standards. They are set out initially in a way that is independent from considerations of the use of ICT. However, the links with ICT are usually very clear. If, for example, one accepts that better geography would involve direct access to the views of a person in another country rather than reading about their views as edited by a textbook author, then the use of ICT is clearly going to raise the standard. Even further, the use of ICT may, in some respects, define and set the standards towards which every student should be working.

Difficult questions

The argument that ICT can raise and define the standards in some aspects of work in geography raises some difficult questions. Although computers are now widespread in both homes and schools, it is still the case that not all students have easy access to them, or to the particular software that is needed, such as GIS software. One can argue that students should not be penalised because they do not have access to ICT, but this is an argument that needs some thought. It raises the question as to why the standard should be kept down because of this 'digital divide'. It begs the question as to whether a hand-drawn graph, with all its imperfections, can ever be given the same mark for its technical quality as one that has been drawn using ICT. While there are other criteria against which a graph or map can be marked, this is one in which the use of ICT is hard to equal. It is difficult to justify penalising excellence by setting the standard at a lower level. A similar argument can be used for other aspects of work in geography where working with ICT can clearly do something better.

New directions with ICT

A further question to ask is whether the use of ICT can provide opportunities for geographical study that are not available without its use. It is, for example, impossible to process satellite imagery without the use of ICT. The data is in digital form and it requires special software to create an image. If the processing and analysis of satellite imagery is accepted as being 'good geography', then it follows that students who are not able to do it will be missing out on something. Quite simply, they cannot achieve this aspect of good geography if they are not given the opportunity to achieve it. The same argument can be made for the use of GIS and, to some extent, for other aspects of geography in which ICT can play a major and sometimes irreplaceable part.

Multi-media for multiple intelligence

There is every educational sense in making use of ICT in teaching and learning. Theories about multiple intelligences suggest that students learn best in a variety of ways using different forms of intelligence. A related set of ideas divides learners into those who respond best to visual, auditory and kinaesthetic (VAK) techniques. Even without accepting every detail of these theories, teachers with any level of experience know that, in every class of students, some are good at listening, some learn more by looking and some prefer a 'hands on' approach. They also prefer different kinds of learning activities that engage them in the material. Using a variety of teaching strategies is one means of maintaining interest. Although the variety of learning styles is likely to be greater in a mixed-ability class, there will still be considerable differences in a class that has been set or streamed. Even in a class that has been set according to students' mathematical or linguistic abilities, there will still be differences in the types of intelligence that the students use in studying in those subjects.

The use of ICT is one way in which geographical material can be taught so as to access the different types of intelligence and cater for visual, auditory and kinaesthetic learners. The multi-media nature of digital resources is obviously beneficial with regard to visual and auditory learning. The benefits for kinaesthetic learning are not so obvious in the conventional sense of 'hands on' experience. Yet students who work with computers appear to find that their control of operations through keyboard commands is at least a good substitute for a direct tactile experience. The cut and paste tools on screen simulate what they can do with scissors, while dragging and dropping can simulate the physical movement of an item. Although there appear to be some differences between how boys and girls work with ICT, both appear to respond positively to it. There are, of course, as with every type of teaching and learning strategy, many exceptions.

There is clearly every advantage in using a range of ICT applications and tools so as to present a variety of resources and activities. The four main challenges for teachers are:

- to identify what ICT can do well
- to acquire the necessary hardware and software
- to learn the skills and techniques for using it
- to understand how to teach the students to work with it.

This is no mean task, but it is one that many geography teachers have already embraced and achieved successfully.

A curriculum that makes sense

The fragmented nature of the secondary school curriculum is a common cause for complaint among educationalists and also among students themselves. This problem is not easy to resolve, partly because fragmentation does have some benefits. At least a curriculum based on subjects as defined by NC Orders and Exam Board courses provides a clear structure within which ideas, skills, knowledge and values can be taught. This is the argument for separate subjects and also for the students' right to choose between at least some of the different subject areas that interest them, for whatever reason.

Conversely, the fragmented curriculum leads to what may appear to be a lack of coherence and at worst, the creation of artificial boundaries, not only in the subject content, but also in how it is taught and learned. A considerable amount of guidance has been provided in recent years on how different aspects of the curriculum can be more effectively integrated. This, for example, has been through ways in which the core skills of literacy and numeracy can be taught not only through maths and English, but also across the curriculum.

There are also questions about how ICT capability can best be taught. To help resolve this problem, there is guidance that comes under the acronym of ICTAC, or ICT Across the Curriculum. The underlying principle is that although some discrete ICT teaching is essential so that students can work with the software, it is also necessary to embed and integrate the use of ICT across the curriculum. To help schools do this in a coherent manner, the ICTAC strategy allocates a number of key aspects of ICT to each subject. The allocation has been done in consultation with the subject-specialist professional organisations such as the Geographical Association and the Royal Geographical Society. The guidance is non-statutory, so schools are able to create their own framework, but the principle of developing a whole-school approach is essential. To this end, geography has been allocated four key themes and concepts in ICT, each forming part of the wider ICT framework.

The ICTAC guidance for geography (see Figure 1.5 overleaf):
Finding things out:
- using data and information sources
- searching and selecting
- organising and investigating.

Exchanging and sharing information:
- refining and presenting information.

This does not prevent work in geography from engaging other aspects of ICT, but it may help to create the kind of focus that is needed for subject work with ICT to make sense. If every department is able to 'deliver' its part of the ICT work, then ICT in each subject can be used effectively. It should also be done without taking up subject time to teach the basic ICT skills. Perhaps the teaching and learning can then make more sense to the students, and standards can be raised by a more collective and integrated approach to the curriculum.

Making links

Key Stage 3 National Strategy ICT across the curriculum: ICT in geography

Key concepts in the Framework for teaching ICT capability: Years 7, 8 and 9
The National Curriculum programme of study for ICT groups the knowledge, skills and understanding that pupils need to acquire into four themes:
- finding things out
- developing ideas and making things happen
- exchanging and sharing information
- reviewing, modifying and evaluating work as it progresses.

These themes are subdivided into nine sub-themes.

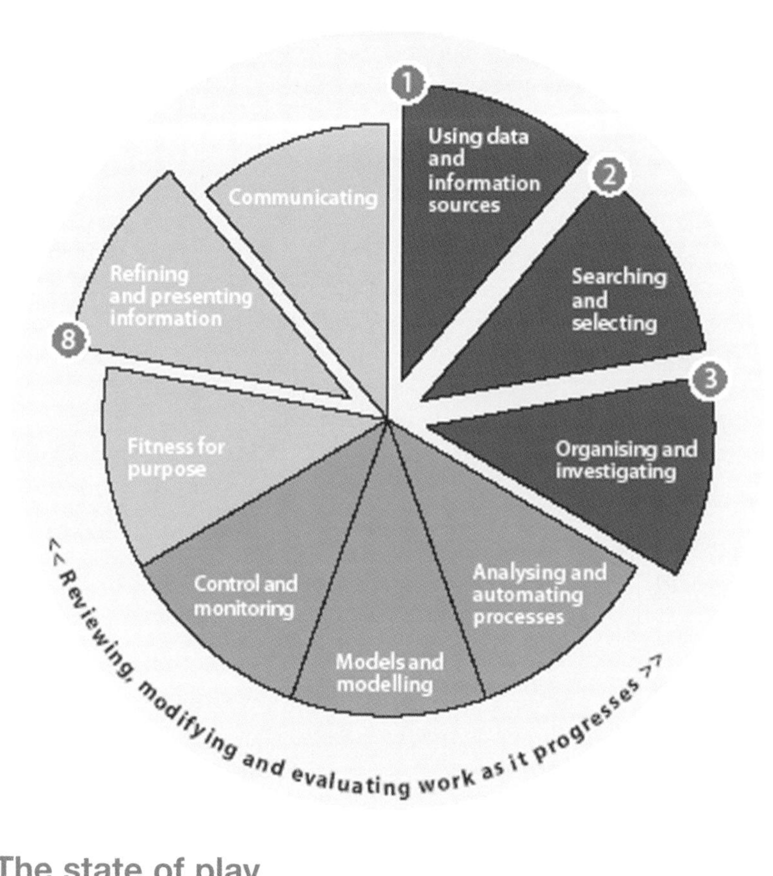

Figure 1.5 *The Key Stage 3 strategy document ICT Across the Curriculum (ICTAC) divides the focus for subjects into different aspects of ICT. This diagram shows the aspects of ICT on which geography could be focused as part of a whole school plan.*
© Crown Copyright 2004 DfES

Check it out

This extract comes from research by BECTA into the use of ICT in geography. To what extent does it describe the use of ICT in your department?

> Ofsted's report on ICT in secondary geography found there were inconsistencies in the quality and use of ICT across schools. In too many cases, the limited time spent in ICT suites is used well to reinforce ICT skills, but there is too little focus on enhancing the delivery of geography. Lack of access at required times is often discouraging geography departments from using ICT. (Ofsted, 2004)

Website
BECTA: What the Research Says

Check it out

Think about the policies for ICT that exist in your school:

- What does the school's ICT policy say about the students' entitlement to ICT?
- Does the geography department have an ICT policy, either separately or built into other policies, e.g. on resources?
- What is the booking system and timetable allocation for ICT rooms?
- What plans are there for the future of ICT in the school?
- Do you have any input to any plans for the future?
- Are you clear about what your input would be?

Making links

Key Stage 3 National Strategy
ICT across the curriculum: ICT in geography

> Many schools continue to cling to a belief that cross-curricular provision can deliver good progression in ICT capability, in spite of inspection evidence to the contrary over recent years. The weight of evidence suggests that what works best is a balance between discrete provision and the application of ICT capability across other subjects. However, many schools continue to struggle to achieve this. (Ofsted, 2001/02)

The state of play

On the whole, geography teachers have shown an enormous willingness to embrace ICT within their subject. It does not take much for most geography teachers to appreciate the power of ICT to show pictures, handle data, draw maps and write text. But in spite of ICT developments over almost three decades, the use of ICT in geography classrooms is still best described as patchy.

There are some schools in which the geography department is a centre of ICT excellence. These are departments where everyone in the department is ICT-literate, the use of ICT is written into schemes of work and ICT has become an essential part of both teaching and learning. Geography teachers in these schools have developed the skills and techniques for using interactive whiteboards, there is a departmental website and a shared understanding of how ICT can both define and raise standards. This is, of course, only possible in departments that have access to the hardware, software and liveware (technical support) that is needed to work with ICT. The support of senior managers can also be a key factor.

At the other extreme, there are geography departments where regular access to ICT resources is difficult to the point of being impossible. Attempts to use

ICT are frustrated by the technical difficulties involved in getting ICT into the classroom and the impossibility of booking an ICT room at a time that fits with the limited hours of the geography timetable. No amount of ICT training seems able to break through this barrier. Indeed, the more ICT training takes place, the greater the demand for the limited resources! So although work in geography is capable of making extensive and effective use of ICT in a way that would also serve the students' wider needs, access is often blocked either by subjects that have a higher profile or by discrete work in ICT.

Give us the tools

In many schools, poor management of ICT resources means that they are needlessly underused. One issue is that reliance on crude student-to-computer ratios can hide the more complex realities of access. The DfES target for August 2004 of one computer for every five students in secondary schools may seem adequate. This figure, however, masks the real problems of access in relation to timetable, specific software, computers that are linked to the internet and other issues.

Although the emphasis on discrete ICT lessons as part of the Secondary (KS3) Strategy for ICT has been a problem for other subjects, more recent thinking on this appears to be redressing the balance. The ICTAC guidance documents present a strong case for a more coherent whole-school approach to the development of students' ICT capabilities. The theory is right, though matching guidance against resources may well be a considerable challenge in many schools. Although the initial emphasis on discrete ICT work has been modified, there has not been the right level of spending on hardware and the other basic requirements to ensure that both discrete and subject-focused work can be done. Without constant access to ICT, teachers are unable to develop the skills they need to work confidently with students.

Making the case

This book cannot offer solutions to the problem of access to computer hardware and specialist software. It can offer ways in which maximum use can be made of limited software at an affordable cost. More importantly, it can identify ways in which work in geography can be enhanced by the use of ICT. These arguments will enable geography teachers to make a strong case for the resources that they will need for the subject not only to survive but to grow.

If the case for raising standards in geography is not felt to be important, then geographers must argue that their subject offers a much-needed context for ICT. It is worth remembering that ICT as a subject is largely devoid of its own body of concepts and contexts for use. Geography is one subject that can provide reasons for using ICT. Indeed, it is one of the best subjects for this purpose. Students appear to learn best when there is a reason to learn, rather

Check it out

NOF (New Opportunities Fund) training for ICT is now mostly over. The spending on e-learning credits is also over.

- What new ICT skills and knowledge of software has this brought to your department?
- To what extent have you been able to implement these new skills and ideas?
- What further gaps are you aware of in your ICT capabilities?
- What further plans do you have to continue to develop your ICT capabilities?
- What new resources have you been able to buy?
- What are your plans to make use of these new resources?

Check it out

Think about the ways in which your geography department could make use of an intranet.

- Does your school have a website?
- Is there a departmental section?
- What is in it?
- How could it be used?

Look at some geography departmental websites from other schools and other sources to see what others are already doing. What are the features of these websites that you think would be most useful to adopt?

Websites

Welcome to Geography
The website of Hampstead School's geography department
Royal Geographical Society
Access to a number of school websites
East Bergholt High School
Report of a geography field trip to Dunwich Heath
Wycombe High School
Hewett School
GeoInteractive
Juicy Geography
The Warwick School
Chelmsford County High School
John F Kennedy School
Raincliffe School
Emerson Park School
Kay's AS and A2 Geography
Goffs School
Netherhall School & Sixth Form College

than being given an abstract task that they perceive to have been set up as no more than a vehicle. Besides, there is little point in developing skills and techniques if there is no context in which to apply them.

To get the right level of ICT resources, the head of department may need to argue a strong case with the school's senior managers. In a situation where there is always competition for limited resources, it can take exceptional and persistent negotiating skills on the part of a head of department to lay claim to whatever resources are available. Unfortunately for geographers, most other subjects can also make the same claim. The ICTAC plan for a co-operative whole-school approach should help, but it is likely that the usual power politics will still play a part in determining how limited resources are allocated.

Check it out

The claims made for the purposes and benefits of using ICT often appear to be extensive. The list below comes from the DfES's *NC in Action* website. Read this list to see the claims made for ICT and check them against your own experiences with ICT.

ICT Learning

ICT helps pupils learn in geography by providing and extending access to large quantities of information. It can help them investigate, organise, edit and present information in many different ways.

Using ICT can help pupils to:

- access, select and interpret information
- recognise patterns, relationships and behaviours
- model, predict and hypothesise
- test reliability and accuracy
- review and modify their work to improve the quality
- communicate with others and present information
- evaluate their work
- improve efficiency
- be creative and take risks
- gain confidence and independence.

In geography, ICT can help pupils to:

- enhance their skills of geographical enquiry
- extend their graphical and mapping skills, and their skills in statistical and spatial analysis
- provide a range of information to enhance geographical knowledge and provide raw material for investigation
- provide access to images of people, places and environments and how environments change
- support the understanding of geographical patterns and processes, and environmental and spatial relationships
- enable them to simulate or model abstract or complex geographical systems or processes
- enable them to communicate and exchange information with other pupils and adults in their own school and in similar/contrasting regions
- contribute to pupils' awareness of the impact of ICT on the full range of human activities and the changing patterns of economic activities.

Chapter 2 Working with words

Key questions

- How can written work be used to communicate different aspects of a student's skills, knowledge and understanding in geography?
- What are the criteria against which quality in written work in geography can be assessed?
- How can written work in geography link to the Secondary (KS3) Framework for English and standards of literacy?
- What are the different ICT applications that can provide the tools to help to raise standards of written work in geography?
- What are some of the issues in using ICT when writing text?
- What opportunities does ICT offer for other forms of communication, e.g. reading and talking?

ICT applications

- Word processor
- Desktop publishing
- Interactive whiteboard software

Focus on words

This chapter focuses on how students can use ICT to improve their ability to communicate geographical skills, knowledge and understanding in their written work. Work with ICT in relation to reading and talking is mainly discussed in other chapters. Although evidence from oral contributions can also provide evidence of students' abilities, it is usually through their written work that their achievements are formally assessed. Whether this should be the case is a discussion for another time and place.

Written work in geography involves different aspects of skills, knowledge and understanding. One aspect of *skills* is the fact that students need to be able to write using the correct geographical vocabulary, this being defined as a 'skill' in the NC Orders for Geography. Skills also include the ability to ask questions and write them down. Students' *knowledge* can be demonstrated by their ability to describe, compare and contrast geographical features and processes. Their *understanding* includes their ability to explain, apply ideas, evaluate and reach conclusions, as well as to both appreciate and express the values and viewpoints of others. In effect, a student of geography needs to be highly literate, and develop good writing skills, in order to demonstrate high standards in the subject.

Although the focus in this chapter is on writing text as prose, it should be appreciated that text is also needed with maps, photos and other graphics – for example, as notes or annotation. There is also a considerable overlap between the contents of this chapter and that of most, if not all, of the other chapters – for example, on topics such as processes and research. The emphasis in this chapter, however, is on how the use of ICT can help with the process of writing in the different genres that are required in geography, rather than on the geographical ideas, knowledge and understanding.

Quality in geographical writing

Many aspects of good-quality geographical writing are common to other subjects. A simple example is good sentence construction, without which it can be difficult to decipher meaning. There are also some aspects and genres of writing that are common across all subjects, but which are particularly important in geography. These appear to have expanded considerably in recent years as the scope of the subject has been broadened to include, for example, the awareness of values and viewpoints, and the use of 'alternative texts'. But within these broad parameters, it should still be possible to identify features of geographical writing that can define its quality.

Spelling and grammar

The basics of spelling and grammar are a vital component of any definition of good-quality writing in geography. Although one can argue that the assessment of geographical knowledge and understanding should be divorced from these basics of written communication, the reality is that poor spelling and grammar can serve to make meaning unclear. The difference in spelling between corrasion and corrosion is only one letter, but it is an obvious example of how incorrect spelling can alter the meaning. At worst, poor spelling of a geographical term may indicate that it has not been properly understood or correctly pronounced. Poor grammar may change the meaning of a sentence – for example, when punctuation is used incorrectly.

Students need to have good spelling and grammar to gain marks in GCSE exams, though oddly enough the same assessment criterion does not appear to apply to post-16 work. Competent use of written English, however, is part of the wider key skills work that should form an integral part of every student's post-16 courses. There is also no specific mention of spelling and grammar in relation to assessment for NC levels in geography, though there are wider processes in place to ensure that standards of writing are improved.

The need for structure

Text that communicates ideas and information, and that shows understanding, needs to be presented in a structure that makes sense. This usually means ordering the material in an appropriate sequence. The enquiry process as set out in the NC Orders for Geography provides a ready-made structure with which to work. This starts with asking a question and following through with research, presenting and analysing the material, then reaching

Making links

NC Orders for Geography: KS3 PoS

Geographical enquiry and skills:
- Communicate in ways appropriate to the task and audience [for example, by using desktop publishing to produce a leaflet, drawing an annotated sketch map, producing persuasive or discursive writing about a place].

In developing geographical skills, pupils should be taught:
- to use an extended geographical vocabulary.

Making links

Key Stage 3 National Strategy Literacy and learning in geography

Learning through writing:
- using writing as a tool for thought
- structuring and organising writing
- developing clear and appropriate expression.

Making links

Key Stage 3 National Strategy ICT across the curriculum: ICT in geography

Refining and presenting information
The use of ICT allows pupils to convey the outcomes of geographical enquiry, using a range of media and presentation techniques. Pupils can communicate similar content in ways that have a different impact, depending on the specific task and the audience. Pupils can use presentations to convey a variety of values and attitudes. They can refine and adapt their presentations according to need and the impact they want to make. They can use ICT to draft and redraft their work. They can use their ICT capability to decide which software to use to present information and thus further develop their understanding of how the chosen medium may affect the outcome.

Making links

NC Orders: Thinking Skills

Reasoning skills enable pupils to:
- give reasons for opinions
- draw inferences and make deductions
- use precise language to explain what they think
- make judgements and decisions informed by reasons or evidence.

conclusions. Most types of geographical writing have an appropriate structure – for example, the description of a climatic graph or the presentation of an argument. It is important for the structure to lead the reader through the content in a way that is both coherent in its flow of ideas and exemplified at appropriate points by case studies and other geographical content. Writing frames can help to guide students in the development of appropriate structures, though the aim must be to ensure that the students can eventually work without writing frames.

Teaching idea

Create multiple-choice spelling tests in Word. Do this by creating a document that students can access and complete on-screen. The Forms toolbar from the View menu contains a tool that allows you to create drop-down multiple-choice text. Students could be given a choice of three words, only one of which is spelt correctly.

For each topic, build up a bank of words that are commonly spelt wrongly. For example, words to do with ecosystems might include:

- Equator
- vegetation
- coniferous
- succession
- habitat
- biodiversity
- deforestation
- savannah.

The right reading age

It is important for students to understand the meaning of ideas and information. This means that the teacher should be aware of the reading age of text with which the students are working. With the increasing use of websites, it is also important for students themselves to be able to recognise when some text is too difficult for them to read and interpret because it was written for a different audience. Perhaps this very recognition may bring home to them the futility of cutting and pasting text that they cannot understand, then including it as part of their own work. There is clearly a margin of difficulty that always needs to be pushed forward, but the rate of progress needs to be realistic.

The geographer's style

Good-quality geographical writing has a particular style that is based on the subject's central and overlapping position between the arts and sciences. It is a style that combines the literacy skills needed to engage in rational argument with the use of factual material to back up the argument. This style includes using case study material with the inclusion of references to real places and events, as well as providing, describing, analysing, interpreting and applying

Check it out

Think about how the KS3 Strategy Framework for Teaching English, Years 7, 8 and 9, has affected your work in geography.

- Are you aware of the different genres of writing that students are taught to use?
- Do you know the characteristics of each genre?
- Can you relate the genres identified in the Framework for Teaching English to writing activities in geography?
- Are there explicit references to the Framework for Teaching English in your Schemes of Work?
- In what ways do the activities you set, and your marking, reinforce the Framework for Teaching English?

Making links

KS3 Strategy: Literacy in Geography

Ideas about why literacy is important:

- The use of vocabulary, expression and organisational control to cope with the cognitive demands of the subject.
- Reading enables pupils to learn from sources beyond their wider experience.
- Writing helps to sustain order and thought.
- Language enables pupils to reflect, revise, evaluate the things they do, and the things that others have said, written or done.
- Responding to higher order questions encourages the development of thinking skills and enquiry.
- Improved literacy and learning can have an impact on pupils' self-esteem, motivation and behaviour. It allows them to learn independently. It is empowering.

Of these, note the importance of writing in those aspects of geography that are related to the affective domain.

Technique tip

You can check the reading age of text by using the Reading Age index in Word:

- Select the text you want to check.
- Click on Tools, then Spelling and Grammar.
- Click on Options.
- Check the box beside Show readability statistics, then click on OK.
- If you run the spelling and grammar check, the Readability statistics will appear when this has been completed. One index is the Flesch-Kincaid index for grade levels; to get an approximate UK reading age, add five to this figure.

statistical data. It also needs to be able to do this in a way that is clear to a reader who may not have a deep scientific understanding of the processes involved.

Clear geographical writing needs to be broadly inclusive, rather than in an exclusive style that is only intelligible to those who are completely immersed in the technical terms, concepts and understandings that are unique to a subject. This is not to argue that good-quality geographical writing should reduce the subject to a lowest common denominator. It *is* to say that the style needs to be appropriate to the holistic nature of the subject, recognising the need to communicate with people who may be specialists across a wide range of academic disciplines and work environments.

Notes and bullets

There are several occasions when geographical text is best provided as short notes and annotations. A set of bullet-pointed comments or a diagram can do this effectively. These short notes should provide key points, such as the reasons for a river flooding or factors that explain the siting of a new business. Identifying the key features or the core of a discussion can show that a student has really understood what is important and is able to communicate it effectively.

Genres in geography

Students of geography are increasingly expected to be able to read and to write in a variety of genres. A list of these genres is set out in the KS3 Framework for Teaching English. Some, such as descriptive or other non-fiction styles, are an essential part of work in geography. The conventions set out for writing in these genres are applicable across all subjects, including geography.

There is also a case to be made for students of geography developing an understanding of some genres of fiction writing. (When used in geography, these genres are sometimes called 'alternative texts'.) Novels and poetry, for example, are able to convey a different type of meaning or perspective on a landscape or on geographical events. Styles used for advertising are important as they can help create an image of place – perhaps sometimes deliberately concealing a wider truth.

By learning to understand the conventions of these different genres, students of geography can develop the critical awareness that is necessary to separate fact from fiction, viewpoints from certainties, balance from imbalance and accuracy from hype. The ability to write in these styles is likely to increase their awareness of how and why they are used – for example, when they are encountered on websites.

Making links

NC Orders for ICT: KS3 PoS

Exchanging and sharing information
Pupils should be taught:

- how to interpret information and to reorganise and present it in a variety of forms that are fit for purpose
- to use a range of ICT tools efficiently to draft, bring together and refine information and create good-quality presentations in a form that is sensitive to the needs of particular audiences and suits the information content.

Figure 2.1 *Different genres of text are available from different websites, e.g. from online newspapers.*

Teaching idea

Give the students some text about the same topic or place that has been written using different genres of writing. The different styles might include:

- a description for tourists
- a news report
- a work of fiction
- a scientific or geographical report.

Compare them to see which one:

- gives the most data and information as facts and figures
- uses the most adjectives to describe the features
- gives the best explanation to make clear what is there
- uses the most specialist language
- is easiest and most entertaining to read
- is the most biased, giving only one side of an argument
- is the most balanced and best argued.

Websites

CNN.com: World
World news reports
Encarta: Encyclopedia Article Center: Geography

Making links

Framework for Teaching English: Years 7, 8 and 9
Genres of non-fiction writing:

- instruction
- recount
- explanation
- information
- persuasion
- discursive writing
- analysis
- evaluation.

Using ICT for text

Almost every type of ICT application has tools that can be used to write text. Some such as word processors or desktop publishing (DTP) programs are mainly designed for text, though they have other capabilities as well. Others such as web authoring and presentation programs are designed to combine text, illustrations and other types of resource. Even drawing programs usually have a tool for writing text. The main emphasis in this section is on ICT applications that can be used to improve the quality of a student's writing in geography.

The basics of writing

The basics of spelling and grammar can be helped to a large extent by the use of the spell-check and grammar-check tools in a word processor and other ICT applications. Although neither tool resolves all problems, they can do much to reduce errors to a level that makes the work easier to read. Perhaps more importantly, these tools can give a degree of confidence to students whose literacy skills are weak. This confidence may help them to write more without the fear of negative marking that focuses more on the English than on the geographical content. Although the ideal is for students to learn to spell correctly and to use proper grammatical constructions, there are times when the geographical content should take priority. Though it is increasingly easy to forget, the study of geography needs to be more than just a vehicle for the development of other skills.

Edit for meaning

The process of writing using a word processor is in some ways different from writing by hand. It has a fluidity that is retained until it is finally printed. Even then, it is easy to edit and print again, or even to leave unprinted. This fluidity allows students to think and make preliminary notes without having to worry too much about the exact words they are writing. Words can first be set out on a concept map, or even as a jumble of key words and ideas, before a serious attempt is made to put them into a more coherent form. Doing this on an interactive whiteboard in front of the whole class can be a useful way to model the process of organising one's thoughts. Students should already be familiar with the idea of drafting and redrafting from their work in English. Editing can take several forms. Text can be edited in individual sentences to make their meaning clear. Sometimes the text may need to be completely restructured by moving whole paragraphs so they are read in a different order. The facility for restructuring work so easily can be used to motivate students to improve their work without needing to rewrite it completely.

Technique tip

It may help some students to identify their grammatical errors and issues of writing style if a Word document is set to identify more than just the basics. Some errors are set by default, but others may need to be set separately. Some of these settings are to check for:

- clichés
- colloquialisms
- sentences beginning with 'And', 'But' and 'Hopefully'
- unclear phrasing
- wordiness.

These settings are found in the Options part of the Spelling and Grammar tool in the Tools menu. They deal with matters of style that may help some of the more academically able students to develop an appropriate geographical style of writing.

Teaching idea

Making links between different topics is an important part of work in geography. Students can create an initial concept map about a geographical topic to structure their ideas. This can be done in any ICT application, either on an individual monitor or on an interactive whiteboard. Some specialist software exists that allows a concept map to be produced – for example, the SMART Board concept mapping program.

Making links

NC Orders for ICT: KS3 PoS

Reviewing, modifying and evaluating work as it progresses

Pupils should be taught to:

- reflect critically on their own and others' uses of ICT to help them develop and improve their ideas and the quality of their work.

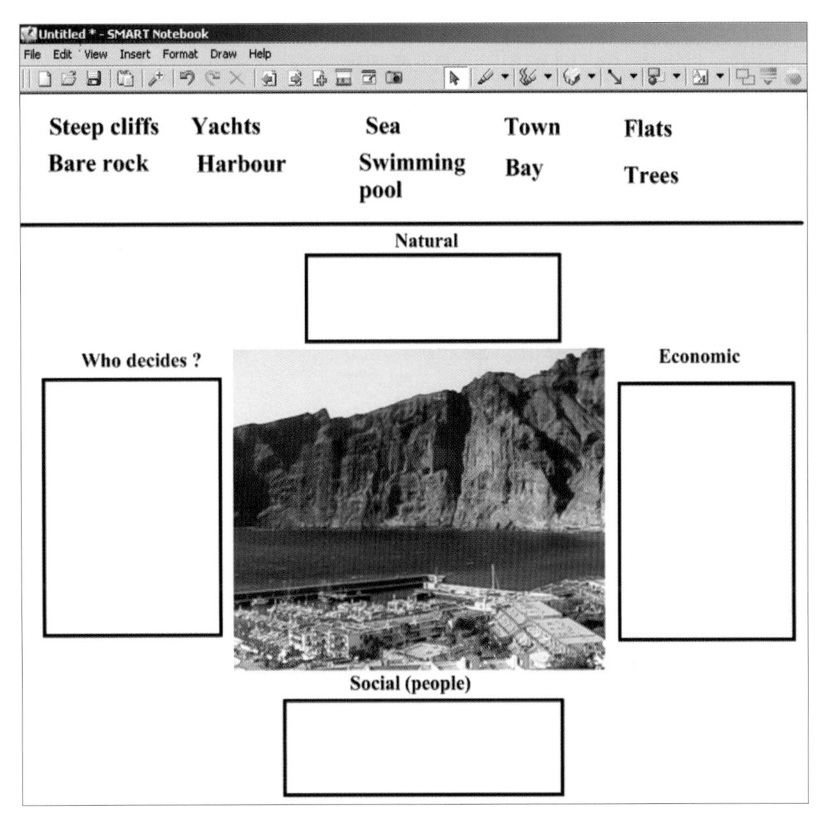

Figure 2.2 *Interactive whiteboards (IWs) can be used for different kinds of word-play activities such as drag and drop, 'blockbusters' and photo games. The example uses SMART Board Notebook to create a simple drag-and-drop activity based on geographer's compass rose idea.*

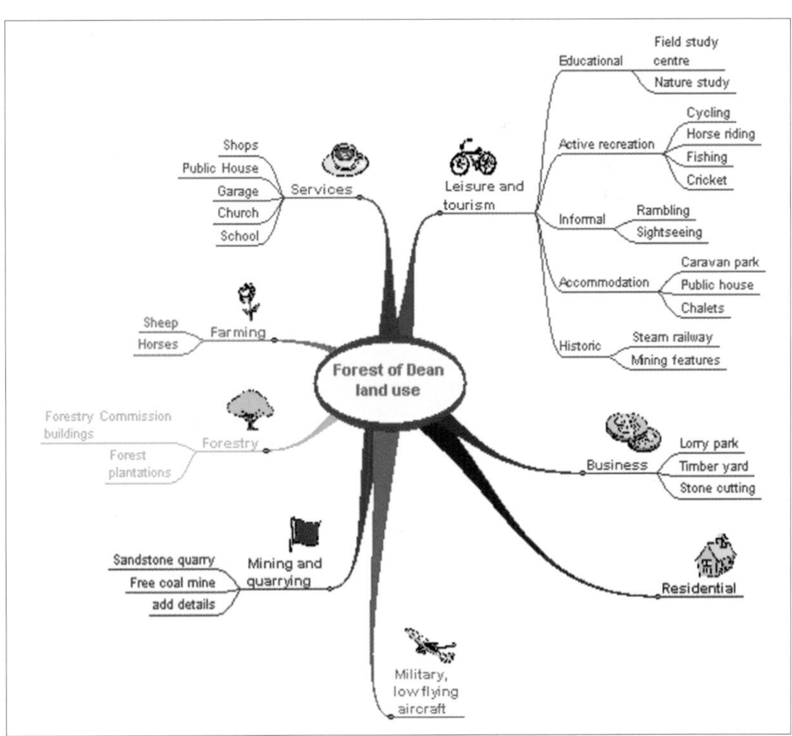

Figure 2.3 *Mind mapping can be done in a word processor, in a drawing program or in special software such as SMART Board or the MindJet MindManager program that was used to create this diagram.*

Templates and frames

A stepping stone towards improving a student's ability in geographical writing is to provide guidance in the form of a template or writing frame. It is easy to set this up in a word processor – for example, by starting sentences with key words that provide clues to what is expected. Useful stem words can also be provided, such as 'because', 'since' and 'as'. The students themselves can make use of the thesaurus in a word processor to help build their own vocabulary. The type or extent of guidance can be varied by writing differentiated versions of resources.

Teaching idea

Show the students two photos of a similar type of landscape. The activity is to compare and contrast their features. The connective words can be provided as part of a writing frame. The following connective words and phrases are suggested in the KS3 Framework for English:

- in contrast to
- whereas
- however
- on the other hand
- although
- whilst
- unlike
- instead of

Websites

Corbis
Photo library
Lycos: Tripod Image gallery
Photo library

Choice of words

The technique of 'filling in the blanks' is a tried-and-trusted method of helping students to work with text in a way that lets them focus on new words and meanings without needing to write out copious notes that cause distraction. This type of activity is especially useful when working with students with poor writing skills who nonetheless have a sound level of understanding. Word-play activities can be set up in a word processor, whether as 'filling in the blanks' or multiple-choice options. In Word, for example, the Forms toolbar has options for setting up spaces or creating multiple-choice options from which to select. Although a spreadsheet is designed for work with numbers rather than text, the same can be done in a spreadsheet – for example, by using the

Teaching idea

The students can use the text highlighter tool or another tool in a word processor when reading a paragraph. This form of text marking can help them to identify:

- new words in geography
- facts and figures
- opinions and values
- key ideas.

> **Technique tip**
> How to create a multiple-choice drop-down test in Word:
> - Click on View, then Toolbars, then Forms.
> - Position the cursor in a suitable space on the screen.
> - Click on the icon for Drop-Down Form Field.
> - Double-click in the box that is created.
> - Write words in the Drop-Down Form Field option window.
> - Add each word.
> - Click on OK when finished.
> - Complete by clicking on the padlock icon in the Forms toolbar.

Data Validation tool in Excel. This program can also be used to check for correct answers by means of the Conditional Formatting tool.

Word games

ICT can be used to create a wide variety of word games – everything from word searches to crosswords. These can be written in basic generic software such as Word by means of tables, text boxes or other functions. An alternative is to use programs downloaded from websites or bought on CD-Rom. Interactive whiteboard software can also be used to create these kinds of activities, for example, by means of Blockbuster or some other gaming template. These simple word games can be an enjoyable way for students to build up their geographical vocabulary. They can also be written to help develop understanding, for example, by matching reasons to statements. While all of this can be done in more traditional ways, ICT makes it easier to edit, save and present the work in attractive and imaginative ways. Files can be shared, stored on a server and completed by students, either on-screen or as hard copy. On-screen work may have the advantage of automatic and immediate feedback. Students can even be given the option to create their own word games to use on each other.

Teaching idea

Use templates from websites to create a bank of word games – for example, crosswords, multiple-choice questions, word searches, etc. These can be used as simple starter activities or as a means of checking basic vocabulary during a plenary.

Websites

Hot Potatoes
Word game templates with 'lite' versions available as free downloads
Education Bradford KS3 Team
Hot Potatoes quizzes in geography
Test Master
Subscription site
Discovery School: Puzzlemaker

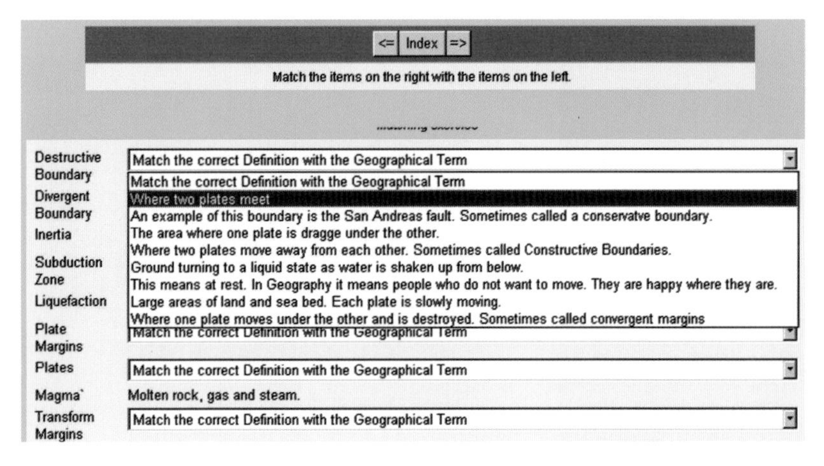

Figure 2.4 *ICT is able to handle short multiple-choice questions using program engines that automatically mark the results. These word-play activities have been created in one of the word games options in the* Hot Potatoes *program.*

Key points text

One way to help students focus on key points is to get them to use presentation software such as PowerPoint. This defaults to bullet-point text in a large font so as to deter them from putting too much text on-screen. Although these parameters can easily be changed, it is probably best to use a different type of program if more text is needed. One key to giving an effective presentation using PowerPoint is to make sure that students do not simply read it out. They should regard it as a visual backup to their oral presentation that will also help them remember what to say. Teachers need to do the same.

Another way to encourage students to condense text into key points is to use the Callout and Text box tools in a word processor. These can be used to label or annotate maps, photos and graphs with text that draws attention to their key features.

Technique tip

Tables in Word are an easy way to create simple drag-and-drop activities. These can include matching single words against their meanings, matching 'heads and tails' of sentences or other activities where words can be brought together.

- To create a table, click on the Table icon or click on Table, Insert and Table.
- Drag out or choose the number of rows and columns, e.g. five rows and two columns.
- Write text in the row you want to use as the template.
- Write the matching text outside the table.
- Students can select text, then drag it into the table.

- Find the point in the square
- Find the four figure grid reference
- See how far the point is from the line on the left of the square to the line on the right
- See how far the point is from the line along the bottom of the square to the line along the top

Figure 2.5 *PowerPoint is one way to help teachers and students to focus their writing on key points by using large bullet-point text.*

Teaching idea

Give students some text about a place or topic. The activity is to reduce the text to a set of bullet point statements on one or more PowerPoint slides. An example might be to take a fact sheet from the Lake District National Park website and reduce it even further to a set of key points and facts.

Websites

Lake District National Park Authority
BECTA: Exemplifying ICT Use in Geography

Technique tip

A visually effective way to include notes or annotation around a photo or diagram is to use a callout from the Drawing toolbar in the standard Office programs such as Word or PowerPoint. A callout is a shape that contains text and a pointer that indicates the feature.

- Click on the Drawing toolbar icon from the Standard toolbar.
- Click on AutoShapes.
- Click on Callouts.
- Choose and click on one of the callout shapes – the most suitable are from the top row.
- Click on the screen and drag out a shape.
- Type text in the shape.
- Click on the outside of the shape, then click on the pointer.
- Drag the pointer to point to the feature.

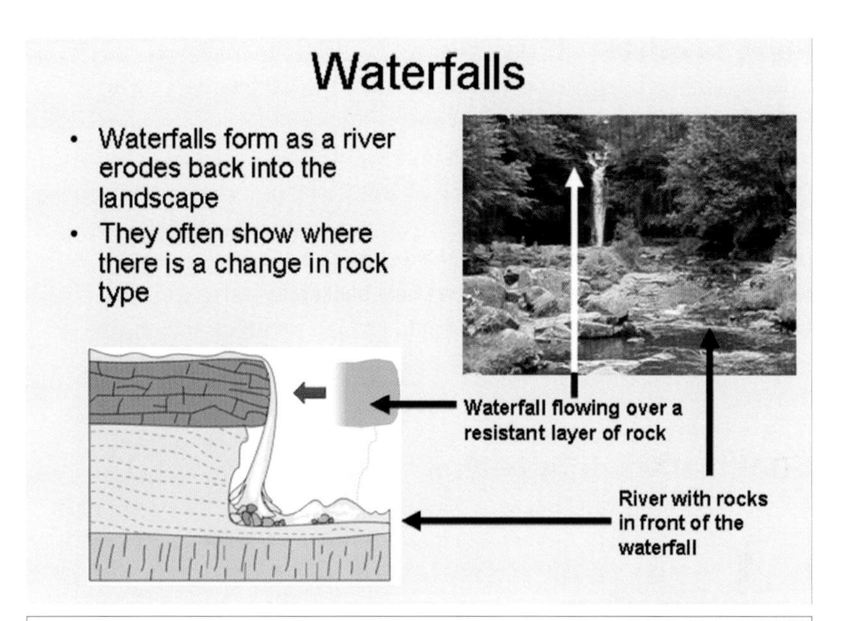

Figure 2.6 *Text, images and other types of resource can be presented together as shown on this PowerPoint slide.*

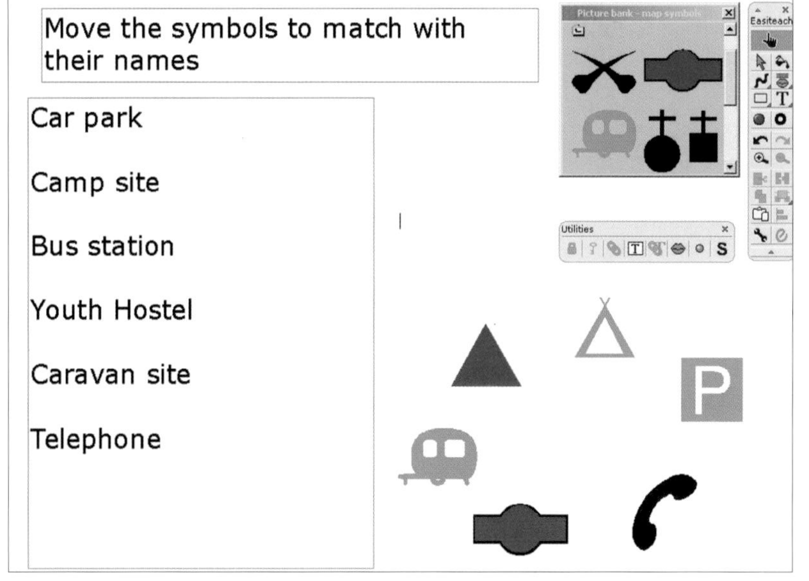

Figure 2.7 *The Easiteach program from RM has clip art specifically for use in the creation and delivery of geography lessons, including these map symbols, map outlines and photos. In addition to the resources supplied in the geography multimedia bank, clip art or photo images can easily be imported from other sources into lesson activities.*

Counting words

The Word Count tool in a word processor can help a student to work within limits, either for a maximum or a minimum number of words. Assessment, for example, can often restrict students to a number of words, as in the case of most GCSE and AS/A2 level coursework. A word limit aims to prevent students from producing too much for a limited number of marks. It can do much to encourage writing that emphasises quality over quantity, and to persuade the student to focus on what is really important. It can also be useful for when work needs to be presented in a more visual form such as in an information leaflet, where space on the page is strictly limited.

Technique tip

There is a Word Count tool in Word, either for the whole document or for selected parts.

- For the whole document, click on the Tools menu and click on the Word Count tool.
- For part of a document, select the text, then click on the Word Count tool.

Lists to sort

Creating lists and arranging the items in order is made easy on a word processor thanks to the Sort tool, which may be used on text or data that is presented in a table. This could be a glossary of terms that need to be in alphabetical order or the names of countries with population and other data. The Sort tool, when used in a table, is a quick way of presenting the data in different ways – for example, by sorting the data based on different columns. A simple correlation activity could be to sort two sets of data about countries so that they can be seen alongside each other. A visual check on the names of the countries may indicate if there is any kind of link that merits further statistical processing and analysis.

Bookmark and hyperlink

Text is usually set up to be read in a linear manner, starting at the beginning and reading through to the end. But this may not always be appropriate for a geographical resource that is produced either by the teacher or a student. It may be more useful to be able to move quickly from place to place as the need arises, rather than being constrained by a pre-set order. A resource, for example, can be set up by a teacher so that students can carry out an enquiry. The contents of the resource can be accessed in any order as the student thinks is appropriate. In a similar way, students could create resources that are designed to be used in an interactive and non-linear way. The technique used to do this is to create bookmarks and hyperlinks. This can be done using a word processor, presentation software, web authoring or other multi-media authoring software. Although the tools to set up the links are different in detail, the principle is the same, whichever type of ICT application is used.

Designed to read

Using text to communicate involves more than just writing it. It also needs to be designed so that it is visually accessible to the reader. This can involve designing the page for layout, amount of text, line length and the way the text flows down a page. Even the use of white space on a page can help with readability. Although this does not affect the quality of the geographical content, it is nevertheless important that students should understand that their geographical work should be clearly presented.

The tools to create page layouts can all be found on a word processor such as Word. Line length, for example, can be controlled by the ruler, or text can be put in a box that can be resized, reshaped and moved to different places on the page. Images can also be resized and moved to places that link visually with the text. However, this kind of design work can arguably be done better using a desktop publishing program because of its more specialised tools and options. A DTP program also has design templates that can be

Making links

NC Orders for ICT: KS3 PoS

Reviewing, modifying and evaluating work as it progresses

Pupils should be taught to:

- be independent and discriminating when using ICT.

used to create different kinds of documents such as booklets and brochures. Students should be taught how to use both types of programs, and made aware of the advantages and disadvantages of each so that they can make appropriate choices.

Teaching idea

The students can design an information board to be read by visitors to a beauty spot or a site of special scenic interest. Examples of this might include a coastal landform, a waterfall, a gorge, a cave system, a lake or a beach. The board should consist of the following:

- a map to show where it is
- a diagram and/or photo to show its main features
- a description of the features
- an explanation of how the feature has been formed
- ideas about the need to conserve the site
- guidance to visitors on how the site is being managed.

The students should be able to choose from different ICT applications, e.g. a word processor, a desktop publishing program or a multi-media authoring program. They should understand that some programs are easier to use for page design than others. If this work is co-ordinated with work in ICT, it should not be necessary to spend time on teaching students how to use the program.

Websites

Cheddar Caves and Gorge
Durdle Door
A virtual field visit from the University of Southampton
The National Trust: Orford Ness National Nature Reserve

Blogging

Ideas about different topics can be shared over the internet by means of a weblog, also known as a blog. This is a means of sharing and obtaining direct access to the views of others about different issues. Blogging has become an international phenomenon, made possible by the power of the internet to ignore distance and international boundaries. This in itself provides interesting opportunities for discussion about degrees of political control and the quality of life in different countries. It gives students an opportunity to practice their own writing skills with a direct purpose and the motivating factor of an international audience.

Teaching idea

Get your students to access or even start a geographical blog. One way to start with this is to use the Geo Blogs part of the *Geography Pages* website.

Website

Geography Pages

Wider issues with ICT for text

The effectiveness of ICT in producing a higher quality of geographical writing, even if by indirect means, is hard to question. The most academically able students can edit text to enhance meaning. The less academically able students can use ICT to produce work that looks neat and is readable, even when the geographical content is relatively basic. Although appearance isn't everything, it can be a motivating factor to encourage students to do better. There are, however, some wider issues to address when students make extensive use of ICT to help with their geographical writing.

Technical words

A minor problem with using ICT for text is that technical words in a subject are not likely to be included in the thesaurus or in the spell checker. Also, the meaning of a technical term may often be quite different from its normal meaning. The word 'relief', for example, has a meaning in geography that is not included in the thesaurus. Another example is the word 'depression'. Although it is defined as some form of 'slump' or 'hollow' in the thesaurus, this is a long way from its full meaning in geography. This, however, need not be a major problem, as students are well accustomed to the fact that each subject has its own specialised meanings.

Assessment of English

Although spelling and grammar are not normally among the criteria for assessing work in geography, they do play a part in GCSE coursework. This creates a professional issue for the teacher who marks it. Work written using a word processor is likely to contain fewer of these kinds of errors than work written by hand. The problem is one of comparing work that is done by hand with work produced using a word processor. Since GCSE coursework also contains recommendations that ICT should be used, there is clearly the potential for confusion! One can argue that it is the end result that is important, not how it was produced. This argument would make the use of ICT acceptable and indeed desirable. One solution to achieve fairness and equality, is to ensure that all students have access to a word processor, even if this means extra time being spent before, during or after school. The solution that prevents all students from using a word processor is not a tenable position to hold.

Appearance against quality

The appearance of work done using ICT creates another problem that teachers need to consider. It is easy to award higher marks to work that looks neater and is easier to read than to work from a student whose handwriting is difficult to read. The solution to this is to establish clear assessment criteria. On the other hand, a student who has word-processed and printed the work may appear to have written less than one who has written it by hand. Again,

Teaching idea

This idea may seem perverse, but for some students it can be a good idea to work with the spell checker switched off! Do this by switching *on* the 'Hide spelling errors in this document' check box. This is in the Spelling and Grammar section of Options. When they have completed the work, they can check their work. This will not improve the quality of their geographical thought, but it will help them to identify words that they are spelling incorrectly but that are being instantly corrected by the AutoCorrect tool.

teachers need to take this into account when marking. Use of the Word Count tool can eliminate this problem.

It is also important to ensure that the students are given advice on which aspects of their work they should be focusing on. Although their work should always look good, the weighting of marks, and their time priority, should always be based on the quality of the geographical content rather than on its appearance. An exception to this may be where the assessment criteria specifically require a special type of presentation, such as a leaflet or advertising material.

An issue can arise when students are asked to produce a PowerPoint presentation as an alternative means of assessing their abilities. The students may prefer to do this rather than writing text in a word processor. The problem is that, when they produce minimal text as a bullet list of points, their true level of understanding may be difficult to determine. There may also be the temptation to assess their ability to use the tools and functions of the software rather than the quality of the geography. Some types of software are good for assessing some types of abilities, but not every piece of software is helpful for assessing all types of abilities.

Copied and pasted

The standard appearance of word-processed and printed text creates another issue that needs to be carefully monitored. The text could have been copied and pasted from a source, or it could have been written by someone else – perhaps another student, a parent or an internet agency. Most teachers will have sufficient knowledge of a student's capabilities from other evidence to avoid this problem, but it may still be difficult to take appropriate action with certainty. An external moderator of GCSE coursework will have no such knowledge and will need to rely on the professional standards of a student's teacher to guarantee the origin of the work. While it can be useful for students to access 'model' answers from websites and to share good ideas with others, the temptation to submit work without giving credit to its sources is one that must cause problems of reliability in assessment. Perhaps this is a minor problem when set against the advantages that ICT can bring to working with text.

Text, reading and talk

Although the focus in this chapter has been on writing text, this should not be completely separated from either reading or talking. All three are aspects of the development of literacy skills in which work in geography needs to play a part.

ICT can help with reading by providing opportunities for carrying out research on websites. This will often involve reading text that is written in a different style, and sometimes also at a higher level, than in a textbook. The use of ICT for research is discussed in Chapter 3.

The importance of ICT for talking may not seem so obvious, especially if one regards the use of ICT as a largely individual activity. However, talk can be developed in many ways through the use of ICT – for example, in presentations that are supported by ICT. Talk can also be stimulated by discussion when students are working collaboratively with ICT – for example, when they are carrying out research into separate aspects of an issue that need to be brought to together. Talk can also be involved in multi-media work – for example, when students record their own voice-overs for putting on a digital movie or into a resource they create using multi-media authoring software. Another case is when students work together on a planning simulation or decision-making activity; this is discussed in Chapter 7. The view that working with ICT must in any way be confined to an individual working alone on a single computer is far from what can and should take place.

Check it out

Work done with a word processor may not be easy to identify as having been written by a student.

- To what extent do you think that this is a problem in your school?
- What strategies do you have in place to ensure that the work handed in by students for summative assessment is always their own?

Chapter 3 Research and resources

Key questions

- Which ICT applications can be used for data and information research?
- What criteria should define high standards of research in geography?
- What software and techniques are needed to access and use data and information in digital forms?
- How can lessons be planned so that ICT is used effectively to carry out research?
- What new opportunities does ICT offer for students to work independently and take a greater degree of ownership in what they study?
- What skills do students need to be taught so they can use ICT for effective research?
- How can potential problems be avoided when using ICT for research?

ICT applications

- Web browser
- CD-Roms

Focus on research and resources

A large part of a geographical enquiry involves research for data and information. This may involve primary research in the field, research that uses secondary sources, or often a combination of both. Research is one of the main aspects of ICT that has been identified as relating to work in geography in the ICTAC (ICT Across the Curriculum) document. This chapter focuses on the part that ICT can play in helping students to carry out research using secondary sources. These ideas apply to every level of work in a secondary school, up to and including post-16 work.

Although research using ICT can bring many benefits, it cannot, indeed should not, replace other types of sources, such as hard-copy reference books and textbooks. Nor should it be imagined that ICT-based secondary research should in any way replace fieldwork as a source of data. However, when used well, ICT has the potential to provide both complementary resources and different dimensions that can bring real gains to the quality of research work in geography. It is also worth warning that poorly used ICT can be a dangerous tool that can produce little of value and may result in nothing more than a waste of time and a sense of frustration on the part of everyone involved. Fortunately, these are dangers that can be predicted and therefore avoided.

Figure 3.1 *The use of ICT can give students access to data and information about distant places. This includes places on other planets where, for example, some physical processes such as volcanic action can be studied and then compared with processes on Earth.*

Quality in geographical research

The ability to carry out data and information research is a key part of the enquiry approach to work in geography. The criteria for high quality in information research in geography are likely to include:

- the extent, depth and accuracy of the data and information that is found
- data and information that comes in a variety of forms, e.g. as text, maps, diagrams, sound and photos
- the range of ideas and perspectives about different issues and topics
- the use of data and information that is up to date, as well as opportunities to access historic data that might show a trend
- the ability to evaluate the validity of sources.

ICT is able to play an important part in achieving each of these five criteria. Although some of these features could also be achieved by using hard copy resources, the differences are that by using ICT, the research can be:

- carried out quickly using web search engines
- previewed then copied for temporary storage until information has been assembled
- carried out from a student's home, from school or from a library (where ICT facilities are now often provided)
- made more varied by providing multi-media resources that can enrich the topic.

Amount of data and information

The extent, depth and accuracy of data and information that is available on the web is extensive. Obviously, not everything about a topic that is on websites is either correct or appropriate for a particular enquiry. But with careful research and cross checking, there is every possibility that some useful

Making links

NC Geography Orders: KS3 PoS
Geographical enquiry and skills

In undertaking geographical enquiry, pupils should be taught to:

- ask geographical questions and identify issues
- suggest appropriate sequences of investigation
- collect, record and present evidence.

Making links

NC Orders for ICT: KS3 PoS
Knowledge, skills and understanding

Finding things out
Pupils should be taught:

- to be systematic in considering the information they need and to discuss how it will be used
- how to obtain information well matched to purpose by selecting appropriate sources, using and refining search methods and questioning the plausibility and value of the information found.

Making links

Key Stage 3 National Strategy
Literacy and learning in geography

Learning from text:

- developing research and study skills
- reading for meaning
- understanding how texts work.

Making links

Key Stage 3 National Strategy
ICT across the curriculum: ICT in geography

Searching and selecting
The efficient use of navigation, using CD-Roms and the internet, and familiarity with search conventions in order to refine their results, are central if pupils are to develop their geographical enquiry skills to the full.

Making links

NC Orders: Thinking Skills

Information-processing skills enable pupils to:
- locate, collect and recall relevant information
- interpret information to show they understand relevant concepts and ideas
- analyse information, e.g. sort, classify, sequence, compare and contrast.

Enquiry skills enable pupils to:
- ask relevant questions
- pose and define problems
- plan what to do and how to research.

Evaluation skills enable pupils to:
- evaluate information they are given
- judge the value of what they read, hear and do
- develop criteria for judging the value of their own and others' work or ideas.

information can be found on most, if not all, geographical topics and places. If there is little about their own local area, the students could create their own website. Successive cohorts could then build on it from year to year, extending its resources and checking the area for change. Research with the use of ICT is capable of being used at almost every level and certainly from key stage 2 upwards. It is therefore important to ensure that there is progression in different aspects of the research methodology, as well as in the information obtained from it.

Teaching idea

Use postcodes to carry out research in the students' local area. Several web-sites can be searched by typing in a postcode, for example, to obtain maps both old and new, and to obtain statistical, social and environmental data.

A study could compare districts within the school's catchment area, with students taking responsibility for researching their own district. This could be complemented by taking digital images and undertaking field research. An alternative approach could be to take a transect out from a city centre, plotting data for the postcode districts along the route. This could be linked to a maps and vertical air photos to show how land use and population features change with distance from the centre.

If postcodes are not known, they can be found by using the Royal Mail website, which allows up to 12 free searches for addresses in any one day. Searching in this way involves typing in the name of a business or a house number and street name.

Students should note that when using some parts of the *Up My Street* website – for example, for crime data – the figures provided relate to the areas used by the police for data collection, which do not specifically relate to local area postcodes.

The importance of postcodes in itself provides a useful lesson about how spatial data is used, for example, in setting rates for car and house insurance.

Websites

Multimap
  Base maps and vertical air photos
Office of National Statistics
  An interactive map that can zoom to a large scale
Old Maps
  Maps from the 19th Century
Neighbourhood Statistics
Up My Street
Royal Mail
  Postcode addresses finder
Environment Agency
  Map of potential flood areas
Homecheck
  Local environmental data
BBC: Where I Live

Media-rich

Text often constitutes the basic format for information and ideas, but text may not be enough and may not make the ideas accessible to many students. Data and information in a variety of media can add quality to the research. Figures presented in tables and as graphs can add depth to a description. Photos can help students to visualise a place or feature in a way that can complement the text, or even on occasions completely replace it. Photos and maps may also be sources of evidence and an essential part of the geography, such as when trying to convey an image of a place. Animations can help to develop a better understanding of processes, both because of their visual impact and because of their ability to compress time. So although text is the focus for this chapter, it is important to see it in its wider context as one type of resource and means of communication amongst many others.

Teaching idea

Use websites to collect data in different media about an aspect of the weather such as the formation of rain. The resources can include:

- **text** – use search engines to find sites at an appropriate level
- **digital video** – BBC website
- **animations** – Meteorological Office
- **satellite images** – the Dundee University website
- **photos** – search image banks for different types of clouds and rain
- **statistics** – find rainfall data for different locations
- **sound** – sound files from websites or clip art files.

Combine these resources to make a presentation. Groups could carry out research into the different causes and types of rainfall, or focus on precipitation levels in a variety of locations. They could also evaluate the benefits and problems encountered when using each type of resource. This could involve taking their own learning styles into account and considering the needs of different audiences and techniques for presentation.

Ideas and perspectives

Access to a wide range of ideas and perspectives is essential to developing a critical understanding of the complexities of most geographical issues. There are seldom only two sides to every argument. Students need to develop an appreciation that geography involves studying complex issues, and that an understanding of different viewpoints and perspectives can be as important as the basic facts. Some 'big issues' run over decades – for example, global issues such as deforestation, desertification, development, energy supply, global warming and sustainable development. There are also issues such as urban expansion, transport policy and farming methods where different groups have particular viewpoints based on values they hold to be of particular importance.

Organisations such as national pressure groups usually have their own websites to present their views. At another level, local issues can generate

Teaching idea

Students can carry out web research to find out about different viewpoints – for example, on the topic of global warming or whale hunting. The websites below show that there are different viewpoints held by scientists, politicians and others.

The same kind of research can be used for other geographical topics – for example, in issues to do with trade, aid, nuclear energy, the need for more housing, etc. The whale WebQuest (below) is a good example of how students can be guided through their research on a controversial topic.

Web links

Newswise
National Resources Defense Council, USA: Global Warming
World Wildlife Fund: Global Challenges: Climate Change
The National Center for Public Policy Research: Global Warming
BBC News: Norway opens whale-hunting season
To Hunt or Not to Hunt: A WebQuest on Bowhead Whale Hunting in the Arctic
British Geomorphological Research Group: Three Gorges Dam, China

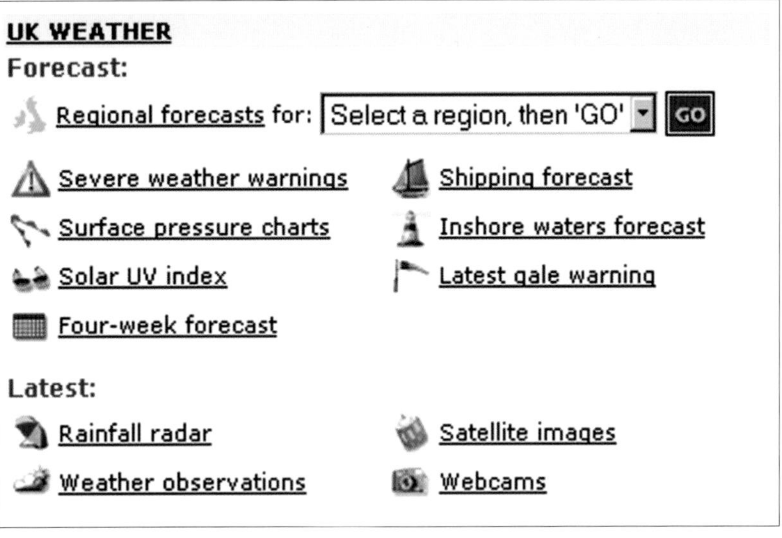

Figure 3.2 *Information is available as it happens. This allows students to find out about current events, especially those such as the weather that can directly affect their own lives. This information can be provided in different types of media. Weather information comes as maps, satellite images, statistics, animations, diagrams and text.*

viewpoints that polarise people in local communities. Temporary websites can be set up quickly as a cheap and effective means of communicating ideas. All these types of websites can provide students with access to other people's viewpoints so that they can form their own values, create their own viewpoints and reach their own decisions.

Up-to-date geography

The content of geography does not stand still, though some historic case studies can certainly be useful to illustrate key ideas. However, students are likely to develop a better appreciation of the relevance of geography if what

Teaching idea

The students can carry out their own research into a local planning issue that has a limited time span – for example, a proposal for a change to local land use such as a quarry expansion or the route for a new road. Some local planning issues can take so much time to be resolved that websites and environmental groups are able to get their ideas online. These sites can be a useful source of alternative perspectives and viewpoints, though students may need to appreciate that volume of opinion does not always represent the balance of opinion in the area. Once the issue is resolved, the sites can go offline again, or the information is removed as attention moves to a different location where there is a similar issue.

Students could search websites to find examples of places where there are current issues such as:

- a quarry expansion
- a new road
- new housing on greenfield land
- an airport expansion
- a new supermarket.

For the issue and the location, they should collect information to show the following:

- background information about the location, e.g. population, economic factors, relief
- details of the proposal, e.g. where it is, its size, appearance, etc.
- reasons for the proposal to say why the work should be carried out
- individuals and organisations who oppose the proposal, with their reasons
- the values of these individuals or groups, if they can be identified
- the techniques used by different groups to present their views, e.g. through the selection of facts, use of photos or diagrams, maps, etc.

Website

British Media Online

National and local newspapers

Teaching idea

Students need to carry out enquiries into the geography of at least two contrasting countries during key stage 3. Access to the web gives students an opportunity to their own choice of countries. There are several websites where suitable information can be found, such as those for Norway, Japan and Brazil.

Before carrying out any research, the students must be clear about the focus for their enquiry. It can be useful to create a template with headings in a word-processed document so that they can copy and paste information and web addresses while they are carrying out their research.

Websites

Brazil

Norwaves

Teaching idea

The Japan Information Network is one source of ideas that come directly from people who live in the country. The ideas are collected from both individuals and organisations. They cover a wide range of topics, some of which are relevant to work in geography. The text is often at a high level, so this activity would mainly be suitable for older and more able students. They could read about some of these ideas to see to what extent they are influenced by the particular perspective of living in Japan.

Website
Japan Information Network

they study is part of their own world, rather than events that happened before they were born. Topical geography is one way to bring classroom geography in direct contact with real events that are current and are within the students' own memory span.

Some of these topical issues may involve the students' own local area and they may be personally involved – a local planning dispute, for example. They may not even realise the extent of their own involvement until they study it in detail and see how many people they know are affected by it, including themselves. Other issues may involve topics that they see and hear about on television news, and that may need some further background information and interpretation in order to be better understood. Older case studies can help to provide historical background to events. But where an up-to-date example is available and appropriate, there must be every advantage in using it. Another way to make use of past case studies is to revisit them with a view to seeing how they have changed. The regrowth of vegetation after a volcanic eruption, or later changes to the landform, for example, can provide useful information about processes of change.

Checking the sources

No amount of data and information is of value unless its sources can be checked for reliability, or at least provided you are aware of any bias that it contains. Research using websites is especially problematic in this respect and students must be fully aware of this problem. It is often difficult, but

Teaching idea

The Royal Geographical Society (RGS) website *Geography in the News* provides examples of current geographical issues with ideas for how to teach them. One of these ideas was to show how the *Spiderman* film was being adapted in India. This gave an interesting perspective on how an aspect of globalisation could be adapted for local circumstances.

Website
RGS: Geography in the News: *Spider-Man India*

Teaching idea

Find information from a website that is completely up to date. Here are some ideas to try:

- the most recently erupting volcano
- a news event from today
- the world's population total
- the weather forecast for tomorrow.

This activity can be used to help students to understand that data presented as facts in textbooks, and also on websites, can quickly become outdated. They should learn that in geography it is preferable to use the most up-to-date statistics, assuming that their degree of reliability can be assessed.

Websites

The Meteorological Office
Royal Geographical Society: Geography in the News
University of North Dakota: Volcano World
USGS: Earthquake Hazards Program
Earthquake maps of current activity
World Population
Constant updates of the world's population

Check it out

Read the list of features that are identified as criteria for high quality in geographical research:

- Do you agree with them?
- Are there any with which you would not agree?
- Are there any other features you would add to the list?
- Do the students you teach have access to resources that would enable them to carry out high quality research?

Making links

NC Citizenship Orders: Attainment targets

KS3: Pupils have a broad knowledge and understanding of the topical events they study.
KS4: Pupils have a comprehensive knowledge and understanding of the topical events they study.

nevertheless essential, to investigate the aims and motives that lie behind websites. At one extreme, some websites are deliberately set up to confuse by creating similar web addresses that respond to similar search words. This happens when one interest group wants to ensure that its voice is heard when a topic is being researched. Most, however, are written with their own views clearly stated. Good-quality research in geography needs to take account of the origin of websites, so that the data and information they contain can be properly evaluated.

Using ICT for research

There are three ways of using ICT for data and information research:

- information CD-Roms
- DVDs
- the internet: web and e-mail.

There are similarities in the techniques needed to carry out research using these three methods. The similarities are sufficiently strong to mean that these techniques can be transferred between the different applications. This is because, although there are some differences in the technologies, the data and information is contained in digital form and is accessed to by means of the same kinds of search tools and engines. This works irrespective of the medium, whether it be movies, sounds, images or text. It is, however, useful to explore some of the characteristics of each type of ICT application before looking at ways in which the techniques can be used.

Information CD-Roms

Information CD-Roms provide a static resource in the sense that, once information is copied to them, it cannot be added to or changed. The disc has a memory that is 'read only' (i.e. a Read Only Memory or ROM), capable of holding about 700 MB of data.

Some information CD-Roms are generic, with information that crosses subject boundaries. The various CD-Rom encyclopaedias such as Encarta are examples of these. They may contain sections that can be researched by subject, but unless they are produced in the UK, they are unlikely to use headings that relate to National Curriculum subjects and topics. The definition and scope of geography, for example, tends to be different in the USA from in the UK. They can, however, be easily searched by entering search words or using their other navigation systems. Other CD-Roms have been written with a specific subject and topic in mind, including geography. At best, they can provide a visually stimulating and interactive resource to help students develop research skills and give them data and information that helps to develop their knowledge and understanding.

Information CD-Roms, although useful, can present a number of practical problems to do with the technology for running them and the tools they require:

- The quality and type of content is variable. The resources they contain may be limited to text and some photos, or may be more extensive with video clips, animations and interactive features. The technology for running video and animations has improved considerably in recent years, though it is still important to ensure that the multi-media resources are of high quality. Sometimes a particular resource is included irrespective of its quality – 'multi-mediocrity' is something to be avoided!
- They are produced with tools and screen designs that, although visually interesting, vary between publishers. This makes them look unique, though with enough experience at using them, their common features become more apparent. They do, after all, need to be user-friendly to the point of being intuitive to use. There is no point in using a CD-Rom whose operations are so unique and complex that valuable teaching and learning time in the subject is lost by the need to work out how to use it.
- Running information CD-Roms on a school network is seldom easy. CD-towers are supposed to handle several CD-Roms at the same time, distributing their data to individual workstations. This is often ineffective, since the time needed to access the data may be too long to make it worth doing. Not all students have the patience to wait quietly while nothing is happening. Loading the entire contents of a CD-Rom onto each computer can use a lot of disk space, especially if several other teachers

want to do the same thing. Although the amount of disk space has increased over the years, it can still be an issue.

It seems as if the short era of subject information CD-Roms is already over. The web now provides so much material that it is proving to be financially unviable for publishers to produce CD-Roms, especially for a minority subject such as geography. Some CDs can perform several other useful and specialist functions, but as a source of data and information their limitations are acting to restrict their use. Some are bought with the best of intentions, but stay unused in their unopened boxes.

Research from DVD

CD-Rom technology has given way to that of DVD. DVDs can store and run high-quality video and sound. They have several advantages over video cassettes:

- They can be run through a data projector onto a large screen (the output from some video players can also be run through a data projector).
- They have controls that allow movement backwards and forwards, moving directly to a bookmarked point.
- It is easy to freeze a frame so that students can focus on it and discuss its contents.
- Video images can be captured as still photos, and can then become part of a hard-copy resource, or given to students as a part-drawn sketch to complete.
- The user can move between different ICT applications – for example, between a DVD and a word processor, or from a PowerPoint presentation to a DVD video or animation.

Desktop and laptop computers now build in DVD capability as standard, including the ability to copy to a DVD. There seems to be considerable potential for further exploration and development of this medium in geography. Some additional comments about digital video are included in Chapter 6.

The internet and the world wide web

The world-wide web (www), now usually known simply as the 'web', is the part of the internet that allows anyone to set up a website on any topic. This is a strength in that it has created a vast resource on almost any topic from worldwide locations. But it is also a weakness in that it can be hard to determine the accuracy and reliability of what is to be found there.

Access to the vast majority of websites, now numbering in the tens of millions, is open and free. These are run by individuals, companies, charities, schools, governments and indeed by anyone who wants to put their own ideas online. Although there are few controls over content, schools can block out at least some material that they think will not be appropriate. There are protection systems that are so effective that they block out useful resources.

Some educational companies and other organisations run sites that are only accessible on payment of an annual subscription fee. The cost of buying into these sites has to be balanced against the opportunities they provide and the quality of what is on them. Buying into these sites raises an interesting conundrum, bearing in mind that open research is likely to be one of the main reasons for using the web. If the research is to be closed, the students may as well use a set of books! Some of these sites, however, do provide a richly illustrated and well thought-out set of resources that can complement other web research. Some provide a more specialist service such as the *Maps Direct* site.

In spite of any caveats, it has to be said that the amount of data and information on the web is both vast and beneficial to work in geography. The problems in using it are mostly to do with finding and selecting what is relevant and is at an appropriate level.

Check it out
You can read reviews of geographical software on the BECTA website. There are many useful sources of websites on geographical topics. The *Internet Geography* website is one that contains a well-indexed range of information on most geographical topics.

Websites
BECTA: Educational Software Database
Internet Geography

E-mail is another digital method of research. It can be used to contact an expert via a website, or an individual or organisation either in this country or anywhere in the world. Research by e-mail can provide a personal, often very rapid, response to a question. On other occasions, it is sufficient to access a bank of FAQs (frequently asked questions).

The ICT techniques for research

With the characteristics of different ICT applications in mind, the general techniques for using them for research can now be explored. These techniques can be listed as follows:

- search and find
- copy and capture
- saving bookmarked sites.

Search and find

A simple web search can use a standard search engine such as Google, though students must also know how to narrow down a search by choosing several key words.

Navigation between websites is simply a matter of clicking on hyperlinked words, such as 'more like this', to follow a research trail or visit other related sites. Teachers can help students by creating a web quest, i.e. a research trail with suggestions for key websites.

Copy and capture

Text and images can be captured in different ways. Text, for example, can be copied and pasted from websites by using standard Copy and Paste tools. Images can be saved as files or copied and pasted into other applications such as a word processor. An alternative is to capture part of an image or the screen using a Capture tool, such as in Paint Shop Pro. This can also be done by using the Print Screen key and pasting the captured screenshot, then editing the screen using a crop tool, such as in the Picture toolbar from the View menu in Word or PowerPoint.

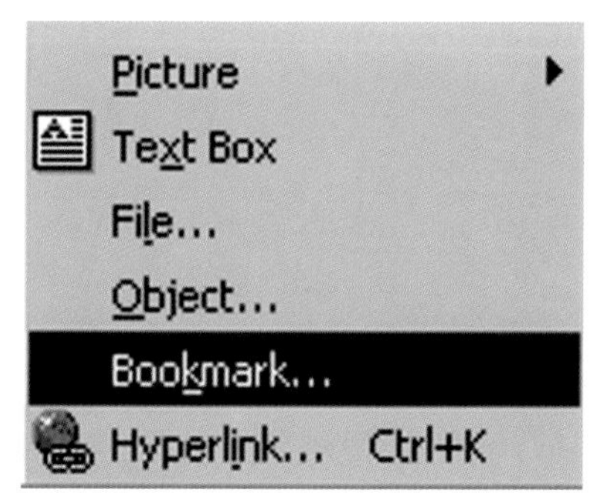

Figure 3.3 *Word provides tools for linking files and moving to places within files. This involves creating a bookmark site and a hyperlink to a bookmark or to a different file.*

Saving sites

Websites that have especially useful material can be saved as bookmarked sites (favorites). This allows the user to return to them later without having to type the web address again. It is also useful to know that web pages can be copied from the screen and pasted into another application such as a word processor or PowerPoint.

Wider issues in ICT for research

Effective use of ICT for research means more than just giving students a title and then turning them loose. It isn't that easy. It involves making a number of decisions over the lesson objectives and outcomes, then devising methods that will best enable the students to achieve them.

Answering questions

Research is likely to be part of the wider enquiry process in which the students are trying to answer a specific question. There may also be a set of sub-questions that involve finding data and information that is needed to answer the main question. Students need to focus on these questions in their research, learning how to start by filtering out material that is clearly not relevant. There may also be a later filtering stage in which only the most relevant material is chosen for use. A final stage may involve further research into questions for which information has not been found.

Steps to web research

As with learning how to ask geographical questions, there are also skills to learn for carrying out the research to answer them. These skills need to be explicitly taught over time. It may, for example, be helpful in the early stages for students to be given a list of websites to use, even if only as starting points. It may even be appropriate to provide specific questions that can be answered from those websites. Doing this, however, should be seen as providing steps that lead students to being able to carry out their enquiry independently, including choosing independently which resources to use and how to access them.

A problem may be that although higher exam grades and NC levels may result from a greater amount of guidance from the teacher, the element of independence that is expected of higher-level work should also not be

Technique tip

You can capture any complete screen, then copy whichever part of it you want to use in another document.

- Open the screen that has the resource you want to copy.
- Press the Print Screen (Prt Sc) key.
- Open Paint.
- Click on Edit, then Paste – this will fill the window with the image you have captured.
- Click on the Select drawing tool.
- Select the part of the captured image that you want to use.
- Click on Edit, then Copy.
- Open a document (e.g. in Word).
- Click on Edit, then Paste (or the paste icon). The selected part of the screen will then be in your document.

You may find that the Capture tool in Paint Shop Pro is an easier way to capture an image. Refer to Chapter 6 to see how to do this.

Technique tip

Write a worksheet in Word so that your students can open it. Copy and paste some web addresses into the worksheet so that they are hyperlinked. Your students will then be able to open websites that you have selected, either by clicking on the web addresses or by copying and pasting them into an open web browser.

Technique tip

This technique is to copy and paste a web address from a web browser.

- Select the web address with the cursor.
- Hold down the Ctrl key and press C to copy.
- Open a Word document.
- Use Ctrl and V to paste the web address.
- Select the web address, then click on the Hyperlink icon on the Standard Word toolbar.

forgotten. This may be an issue to do with the professional interpretation of assessment criteria and standards of marking, especially when the work is to be assessed by the teacher.

Dead-end research

On some occasions when working with websites, it may be justifiable to give little or no guidance for the research. This, however, is likely to be restricted to occasions when the focus of the lesson is on ICT techniques and research skills, rather than on the geography. A successful lesson could arguably result in no new geographical knowledge or understanding about a particular topic. Instead, the students may have learnt some equally valuable lessons about the process of web research, including the message that research is not always successful! Too many lessons like this, however, must be avoided. Quite simply, they waste time and are potentially frustrating and demotivating for the students. It may be better if these techniques are taught in a different context such as in discrete ICT lessons.

Following web links

Websites do not come with any inbuilt structure that reiates to subjects as taught in schools. Links between websites can quickly take a student away from the initial focus of an enquiry. While going off track in this way may waste time, the holistic nature of geography is one that should cause both teachers and students to stop before condemning diversions as being irrelevant. Although organising the school day based on National Curriculum subjects is convenient, this does not reflect the reality of how things work in the 'real world'. Perhaps a more open approach to geographical research might prove fruitful in developing this more holistic understanding of geography, instead of merely paying occasional lip service to links between geography and other subjects such as to science, English and art.

Teaching idea

Use a photo as a starting stimulus for an enquiry.

- Ask the students to suggest some questions to ask about a topic to be studied, using one or more photos to stimulate their ideas.
- Separate out the questions that would be suitable to use for an enquiry; these are likely to be questions about big ideas or decisions to be made.
- Some of the other questions may then become sub-questions to the main questions.
- Open a word-processed document and divide it into sections, each section to relate to one of the sub-questions.
- As the students carry out their research, they should enter web addresses and selected text and images in the appropriate section. This will help to keep them focused on the questions they are trying to answer.

While teachers need to stay vigilant as to where web research is taking their students, it may be worth pausing for a moment when they spot something that seems irrelevant on a student's screen. The route to the 'irrelevant' site could well be worth investigating, and what initially may seem to be irrelevant may turn out to open up new ways of looking at the topic. There are, or course, limits to this open approach to research and the temptation towards online games should always be monitored.

Student choice

One of the advantages of websites for research is it can open up opportunities for students to make some of their own choices. It would seem perverse for teaches to deny them this choice when this is one of the web's key advantages over using a textbook. An element of choice may also help to give the students some degree of ownership of the material they are studying. While this in itself may not directly produce higher achievements or a better quality of geography, the motivation to learn may play an indirect part in producing these end results.

There are opportunities for choice at every level. There is, for example, no need for every student to follow the same case study of a volcanic eruption, the same stretch of coastline, the same city or the same example of a leisure amenity. Nor is there any need for them to study the same country, the same geomorphic processes, the same ecosystem or the same types of employment. Indeed, the learning should be considerably enriched for everyone if strategies are devised to let students share their different choices of study. This can be done by discussion in groups or when a group presents its findings to others.

The challenge is for the teacher to provide a different kind of guidance so that the students are still able to work within a framework. Such a framework is likely to consist of key ideas, concepts and questions, rather than the specifics that relate to each particular place or topic. This may not be easy, especially when working with students who need a high level of guidance. But for students who are able to take advantage of this approach, lack of choice would deny them valuable opportunities for developing their own skills in research, as well as for learning how to apply ideas and concepts. Work that is always tightly directed will not help students to match the higher level criteria, or even to develop the skills required to do so.

Relevant and useful

Once the data and information have been collected, students must avoid the temptation to regard the research activity as being over. It is in fact only just

Check it out

Do you have a long term plan to help students develop research skills using the web? The aim of such a plan is to make them more independent in their research. The statements below show how progression in this aspect of enquiry could be developed over several years as students work on different enquiries.

- Give students one website and a structured worksheet of questions for retrieving specific data and information.
- Give students one key search word to enter in a given search engine. Allow them to develop their own skills in choosing relevant sites to answer particular questions.
- Provide several websites on a word-processed or other document so that students can follow the hyperlinks directly to them. These websites can be located next to the questions to be researched.
- Give students a framework for research but allow them to choose the place or case study to research. Students enter their own search word to find a resource, then find their own websites, which they bookmark.
- Give students a key question to answer with some guidance on sub-questions. Students refine their search skills by entering combinations of words in one or more search engines. They initially select, then copy and paste, relevant material before making a final choice of what to use.

Making links

Key Stage 3 National Strategy Literacy and learning in geography

Learning through talk:
- using talk to clarify and present ideas
- active listening to understand
- talking and thinking together.

Check it out

Carry out a web search for a topic your students are to study. Look at the websites you find. See which ones you think would be suitable for work with students of average ability in a year 9 class. To do this, consider the following features on-screen:
- reading age
- size and style of font
- layout
- design features and colours
- amount of text
- ease of navigation
- amount of information.

beginning. The next stage is to read, interpret it and select for relevance. The temptation to simply copy and paste it is made greater by the simplicity of using the Copy and Paste tools. It will help if students are clearly informed about the marking criteria for the work. Although some credit can be given for finding the material, this should be minimal compared to the weighting of marks to be given for selecting and using the relevant material to answer the enquiry questions.

Acknowledge sources

Students need to understand that there are copyright laws that relate to resources on many websites, even though their own use of the material is unlikely to breach those laws. It is, however, part of the research process that sources should be acknowledged. It is also a lesson they will need to learn as they progress through their educational careers.

Validity of sources

The need to consider values and viewpoints is one of the success criteria throughout the National Curriculum levels in geography. Websites provide valuable opportunities for students to develop their ability to consider values and viewpoints through the need to check that the sources they intend to use are reliable. This, however, is not a simple matter of identifying and choosing websites that are thought to contain unbiased material. It can be argued that there are no neutral websites. Even the most factual website contains a selection of facts that someone has chosen to make available. The degree of bias in these sites may be hard to detect because it was not even recognised by the people who created them. Other sites contain more obvious elements of bias – for example, those run by organisations that want to sell a product. The product may be a place such as a tourist destination. Environmental organisations that have a particular message to convey are usually fairly overt

Teaching idea

The students could use the following (or a similar) framework of questions, to carry out research into a holiday resort they have chosen themselves:
- What is the name of the resort?
- Where is it located?
- How big is it and how many people live there?
- How can people get there?
- How many people visit the resort?
- What are the main types of leisure activities on offer?
- How does the physical environment of the area play a part in the leisure activities, e.g. its beach?
- What are the climate statistics for the resort?
- Is it a popular resort for everyone, or does it mainly cater for people of a particular age?
- Does the resort keep its facilities open for most of the year?

Figure 3.4 *Websites such as CNN give access to news as it happens. Students need to note the origin of their news sources so they can get a balanced perspective on events. What is important for the American CNN site may not be so important on the UK BBC News.*

in presenting their ideas by using selected facts and interpretations to support their case. The distinction between fact and opinion can often become blurred.

Teaching idea

Students can investigate websites from different organisations to see if they can find out how balanced and reliable the data and information on them might be.

- What is the name of the organisation?
- What are the aims of the organisation?
- What are the topics in which the organisation has an interest?
- In which country is the organisation based?
- In which countries does it take an interest?
- How is the organisation financed?

Websites

Greenpeace

Friends of the Earth: Safer Chemicals Factory Watch
Pollution watch for a polluter near you

Noise Abatement Society

Transport 2000: Roads to Ruin

EnCams: Campaigns
Environmental campaigns – litter, clean beaches, etc.

Teaching idea

This idea can be found on the *KS3 Strategy ICTAC* CD-Rom in files marked 'Lesson 2'. It involves carrying out a web search to identify which two of four islands are real and which are fictitious. The activity aims to engage students in evaluating the credibility of web resources by looking at the information about who has set them up.

Students should be taught the importance of cross-referencing material to check for differences in viewpoints. It is even worth checking on basic statistics, and developing an understanding that statistics can be different in different sources. Students need to learn to cope with these differences, rather than constantly seeking the one source that they feel to be the most

Figure 3.5 *It is important for students to learn how to access different sources so they build up a comprehensive understanding of issues rather than relying on one source that is likely to be heavily biased. Although this aspect of ICT is not a focus for geography in the ICTAC documents, it is one that needs to be prominent in any research work for geography.*

BBC NEWS WORLD EDITION

Last Updated: Monday, 10 May, 2004, 17:28 GMT 18:28 UK

E-mail this to a friend   Printable version

Norway opens whale-hunting season

Whaling vessels have left Norway for the Barents Sea to open this year's whale-hunting season, defying an international moratorium and protests.

The Norwegian government has set a quota of 670 minke whales for the season, which runs until 31 August.

Norway's whaling policy has

Iceland Whales Pledge

Visit Iceland. Stop whaling.

GREENPEACE

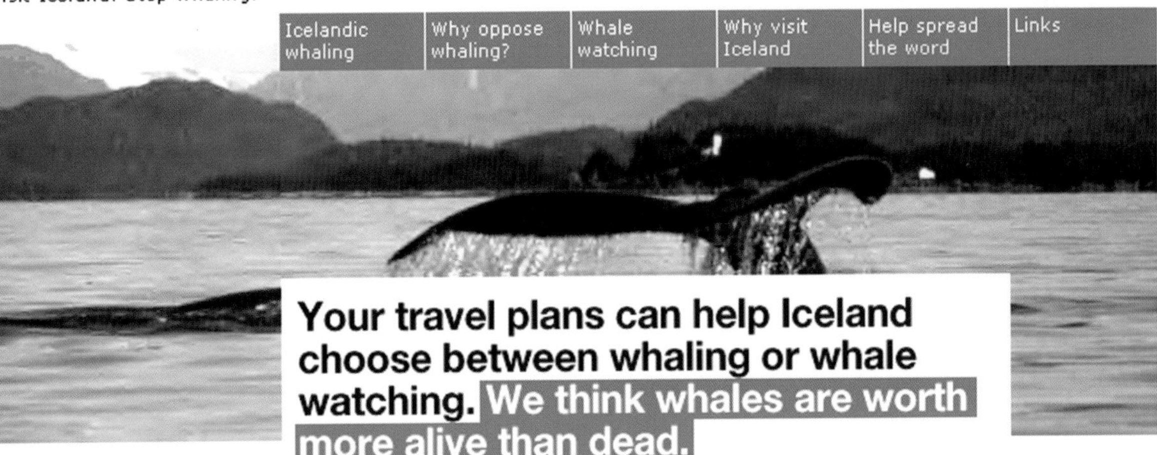

accurate. Engaging in this kind of evaluation of sources should be a sign of good research and good geography.

One aspect of bias relates to the fact that the origin of websites is largely dominated by the USA. Students need to check that their research does not entirely rely on sources from only one country. A search engine usually allows for search results to be limited to a particular country such as the UK. If no such selection is made, students need to take additional care that the data and information they find properly represents a good range of ideas. If nothing else, they should check the spelling!

Be prepared

Both teachers and students need to devise strategies for coping with the fact that, despite improvements in ICT hardware, access to websites is not always possible, at least under classroom conditions. At one extreme, there may be a technical failure affecting the whole web system in the school. A more usual problem is that of slow download times, especially in the afternoons or when the school network is busy with other classes also using the internet for research.

All of these are events for which contingency planning is needed such as saving some web data in a shared area. In an extreme case, it may be best to abandon the lesson before the time is completely wasted or there is general chaos. There will always be another day when the system will work.

Making links

Attainment Targets: NC Orders for Geography

Level 4 They explain their own views and the views that other people hold about an environmental change.

Level 5 They suggest explanations for the ways in which human activities cause changes to the environment and the different views people hold about them. They explain their own views and begin to suggest relevant geographical questions and issues.

Level 6 They appreciate that different values and attitudes, including their own, result in different approaches that have different effects on people and places.

Level 7 They understand that many factors, including people's values and attitudes, influence the decisions made about places and environments, and use this understanding to explain the resulting changes.

Making links

NC Citizenship Orders: KS3 PoS

Developing skills of enquiry and communication

Pupils should be taught to:

- think about topical political, spiritual, moral, social and cultural issues, problems and events by analysing information and its sources, including ICT-based sources.

Check it out

Think about the marking criteria you would use for the students' research. What criteria would you use and what weighting would you give to each criterion?

- finding data and information
- giving credit for sources
- selecting appropriate material
- making effective use of the material
- recognising bias.

Chapter 4 The spatial dimension

Key questions

- How can different ICT applications help to raise standards in drawing maps and in processing map data?
- What sources of maps and other images can be used as base maps?
- What is the range of mapping styles, graphics and colours that are made possible by the use of ICT?
- In what ways can ICT be used to teach about maps?
- How can ICT provide a comprehensive and integrated means of illustrating spatial data?
- How can Geographic Information Systems (GIS) software provide teachers and students with a dynamic tool for drawing and processing map data?
- How can digital technology create 3D maps and photo-realistic landscapes?
- What issues are there regarding the assessment of maps drawn by means of ICT?

ICT applications

- MS Paint, Paint Shop Pro
- GIS software (Arcview, MapInfo, Aegis3)
- MS Word
- Websites
- Google Earth

Focus on drawing maps

The need to draw and interpret maps has been a constant through every revolution in the teaching, learning and applications of geography. Although text, statistics and photos are all of value, maps remain the most effective medium through which to study the locations and distributions of geographical features. The simple truth is that patterns can be most easily seen on a map, rather than being described in words or in statistical indices. In an age when so much data is being presented visually, there is no danger that visual displays of spatial data will go out of fashion, whether as maps, satellite images or vertical air photos.

This is not to say that there will be no changes to how maps are drawn and interpreted. The use of ICT has already shown how maps can be drawn to a better technical standard, and how map data can be processed more efficiently, all in ways that are possible in a school context. The use of ICT has also brought about entirely new dimensions to map work thanks to its ability to integrate different types of digital data. Maps are no longer separate from other resources, such as vertical air photographs, satellite images, Global Positioning Systems (GPS) technology, statistical processing and the creation of landscapes with 3D effects. This section aims to explore some of these new dimensions and the issues that arise as a result of using them with students.

Check it out

Do your schemes of work for key stage 3 contain a progressive and coherent approach to developing map skills that includes the use of ICT to:

- find different types of maps at different scales and from different dates?
- interpret satellite images?
- interpret vertical air photos?
- draw maps to show geographical data?

Making links

NC Orders for Geography: KS3 PoS

In developing geographical skills, pupils should be taught:

- to use atlases and globes, and maps and plans, at a range of scales, including Ordnance Survey 1:25,000 and 1:50,000 maps
- to select and use secondary sources of evidence, including photographs (including vertical and oblique aerial photographs), satellite images and evidence from ICT-based sources [e.g. from the internet]
- to draw maps and plans at a range of scales, using symbols, keys and scales [e.g. annotated sketch maps], and to select and use appropriate graphical techniques to present evidence on maps and diagrams [e.g. pie charts, choropleth maps], including using ICT [e.g. using mapping software to plot the distibution of shops and services in a town centre]

Teaching idea

A map quiz can be used as a simple starter activity on an interactive whiteboard. The *Owl and Mouse* website is one source of simple visual games that involve drag and drop activities. The games can be downloaded and run on the IW with students coming to the front. You can find similar activities on the Ordnance Survey's website or make your own using generic software.

Websites

Owl and Mouse

Ordnance Survey: Free & Fun

Making links

NC Orders for ICT: KS3 PoS

Developing ideas and making things happen

Pupils should be taught:

- to develop and explore information, solve problems and derive new information for particular purposes.

Exchanging and sharing information

Pupils should be taught:

- how to interpret information and to reorganise and present it in a variety of forms that are fit for the purpose.

Making links

NC Orders: Thinking Skills

Information-processing skills enable pupils to:

- locate, collect and recall relevant information
- interpret information to show they understand relevant concepts and ideas
- analyse information, e.g. sort, classify, sequence, compare and contrast
- understand relationships, e.g. part/whole relationships.

Quality in drawing maps

The criteria often used to identify quality in mapping seem to be more a matter of folklore than of a shared professional understanding. The NC Programme of Study for KS3 provides a list of the topics, such as maps at different scales, globes and vertical air photographs, with the requirement that students should be able to draw maps and select appropriate graphical techniques to show the data. But there is no guidance as to expectations regarding quality. Exam board marking schemes are equally vague on the standards that students should be expected to achieve for drawing maps. So it is left to the professional judgement of teachers as to what constitutes a 'good map'.

Drawing maps and processing map data

There are many different aspects of map work. For the purpose of this chapter, only two of these are of relevance to working with ICT:

- the students' ability to draw a map, including the use of quantitative symbols
- their ability to process the map data.

The ability to interpret maps for meaning takes the discussion into a different domain where the role of ICT is mainly confined to the refinement and presentation of ideas (see Chapter 2). Finding maps is a matter of research (see Chapter 3).

Behind this discussion is the need to compare drawing maps by hand (using pencils, pens and a ruler on paper) with using the tools of different ICT applications to draw a map on a computer screen. The contention is that, for the purposes of assessment and defining standards, it is the quality of the finished map that should be important, not the tools that have been used to draw it. It seems right, therefore, that the same success criteria should apply equally to maps drawn by hand and those drawn using a computer. If drawing a map by hand produces the best results, then the computer should not be used. If, however, the best results can be achieved by using ICT, perhaps it is time to raise the threshold against which achievement in drawing maps is measured.

Characteristics of a well-drawn map

In the absence of 'official' criteria for identifying the characteristics of a well-drawn map, the following aspects may be considered:

- **design**: use of space, positioning of text
- **lines**: smoothness, thickness, intensity and styles
- **colour**: the appropriate choice and use of colours
- **signs** and **symbols**: types and how well they are drawn
- **text**: use of fonts and sizes
- **accuracy**: scale, shapes and the amount of detail in relation to scale
- **style**: techniques used to show quantitative data, e.g. as shading or located charts
- **data processing**: tools for measuring and querying the data on the map.

It is assumed that the other map basics will also be in place, such as a map key with scale, directions, etc. Some of the above features overlap – for example, colour can be used in drawing lines and in text. There is also some overlap between design and accuracy, in that decisions over the use of space are bound to affect the amount of map detail that is included. One might also question whether the processing of map data should be included, as this has always been a separate part of mapping. With ICT, however, the two can form part of the same package of operations. In spite of these problems, the above framework provides a means of considering aspects of quality in the drawing and processing of maps so that the potential roles of ICT can be identified.

Map design

A well-designed map should achieve a visually effective balance between having enough space to achieve clarity and the amount of data that is shown. Too much data about too many different themes clutters a map. The amount of space also affects the positioning of text, such as names of settlements or other features. Text that is overprinted or that is too far from the feature will be difficult to attach to its map location. A problem with drawing a map by hand is that it is difficult to edit what doesn't look right. Students often spend a considerable amount of time drawing a map. Then, because they cannot edit it neatly, they may resort to screwing it up and starting again.

Drawing lines

Lines on a map should be drawn to uniform thickness, intensity and colour. This is almost impossible to do by hand unless special mapping nibs are used. There may be different thicknesses for different types of feature, making it even more important to achieve uniformity in each type of line. Different styles of line can include pecked or dashed lines, or a combination of the two. This too is difficult to do well by hand.

Using colour

Colours need to be used selectively in order to achieve a clear result that is also visually pleasing. The choice of colours must be in keeping with the map data. It must also be in keeping with the relative importance of the feature. This involves making choices in relation to the purpose of the map. Although choice of colour is largely subjective, students need to understand that their own taste in terms of aesthetics and clarity may not always coincide with that of others. There are some broad boundaries of convention that should be followed – for example, the use of fluorescent marker inks and other garish colours is best avoided. One basic problem for many students is that they do not bring coloured pencils to their geography lessons. Keeping a class stock in a secondary school is one solution, but loss rates tend to be high!

Signs and symbols

Signs and symbols are the map conventions that give visual shortcuts to map features. Since the same signs and symbols will need to be drawn several times, they should look exactly the same in each position, including in the map key. Doing this by hand is impossible, other than by using stencils or rub-on graphics. Drawing some types of symbol by hand may be relatively straightforward, though attempts to produce symbols in a pictogram style are not likely to be so successful.

Text on maps

Text on a map, like lines and signs, needs to be printed to uniform sizes and thicknesses. The correct positioning is also important. Adding text by hand depends on the student's ability to write neatly – not a characteristic that is shared by all. One problem is that, for the students whose abilities in some basics are lacking, a poorly produced map will simply present them with a visual reminder of their deficiencies. Perhaps a more pleasing result will help motivate students, rather than constantly presenting them with barriers to achieving success.

Degrees of accuracy

Maps need to be accurate in outline, though the degree of accuracy depends on the purpose of the map and on its scale. Drawing an accurate base map by hand can be done by using tracing paper, leaving the problem of then transferring the trace to a plain sheet. A grid can be used, but this is seldom an easy solution. Generally one would expect shapes to be drawn accurately and all parts of the map to be true to its scale. Choices will have to be made over the extent of simplification required – for example, in drawing an area of woodland that may not have distinctive boundaries, or in enclosing an area of settlement where buildings become scattered around the edge.

Check it out

Think about the criteria that you use to assess your students' ability to draw maps:

- Do you have a clear set of criteria that can be applied to drawing maps and processing map data?
- Do you agree that the use of ICT will always produce a map that fulfils higher technical standards than one drawn by hand?
- For what purposes might it be essential to draw a map by hand?
- Do you think that different standards should be applied when assessing maps drawn by hand and maps drawn with the use of ICT?

Styles of mapping

Showing quantitative data on a map involves making decisions over the style that is appropriate, as well as being able to draw that style in a technically proficient manner. There can be a link between the two in that some styles may be appropriate but difficult to draw. Located proportional pie charts, for example, may give an excellent visual representation of the data, but may be extremely difficult to draw on a map by hand. One should, however, expect the data to be drawn in the most visually effective manner. It is probably the case that a student's ability to colour in large areas of a map neatly using the choropleth style has been one of the most obvious criteria used for assessing map quality. It can be what determines the final appearance of the map. 'Colouring in', however, is an activity that, although enjoyable for some, cannot be argued to be either intellectually demanding or an effective use of scarce geographical time.

Data processing

Processing map data involves measuring distances and areas in order to give meaning to the map. It can also involve more complex manipulation of the map data – for example, making decisions over the ranges of data to be used in categories. A simple arithmetical scale is one option, but there are others, such as a geometric or log scale, or even choosing one that is unique to the map data. These decisions affect the appearance of the map, creating what appear to be very different patterns from exactly the same raw data. Students need to understand this principle and to be able to work with it.

Teaching idea

Students can access maps from numerous websites, most of which also contain data and information about countries.

- They could carry out background research about a topical event by looking at one or more of these sites.
- You need to decide on the data that you want them to research, e.g. population totals, GNP, population density, birth rates, etc.
- If they use more than one website, they could check to see if the data is the same on each site. If not, then they could question why there might be differences.
- Ask them to look at the country maps, and compare them to see which gives the most and the clearest information.

Websites

Nationmaster
Cyberschoolbus: statistics
BBC News
Encyclopaedia Britannica
Nation by Nation
CIA World Factbook

They may also need to query the data – for example, only to show data above or below a certain number. Although processing map data could be regarded as a separate operation from drawing the map, it can be argued that a good-quality map should be capable of being interactive, with data processing built in as one of its functions. This is only possible by the use of ICT. Links from the map to other types of resources, such as photos, text, video or sound, are also arguably one of the criteria for a good map. These options could certainly not be argued to be 'bad', as they can add considerably to data and the information that can be derived from a map.

Using ICT for mapping

Most ICT applications can be used to help students learn about, draw and interpret maps and other images that show spatial data. At a basic level, a generic drawing program such as MS Paint can be used to draw maps, either from scratch or by editing imported maps. Even the drawing tools in a word processor can be used to draw shapes and symbols, to create map layers and insert hotspots that link to other data and information.

At the other extreme, Geographic Information Systems (GIS) software is a group of ICT applications that can transform the way in which maps are drawn and map data is processed and displayed. Other ICT applications, such as websites and information CD-Roms, can be used as sources of base maps. The maps themselves are available from the Ordnance Survey in digital forms such as the Master maps that provide land use and other landscape features. Details of height are provided on Digital Elevation Maps (DEM) and Digital Terrain Maps (DTM).

Technique tip

Although maps can be scanned from hard copy, this can create problems when they are used in Paint. The scanning process picks up many light shades of grey, even when the paper seems to be white. This means that the colour infill tool cannot be used effectively unless all the grey pixels have been removed with the rubber tool. Although this is a time-consuming process, it need only be done once to produce a base map that can be used with students.

In short, there is more than enough ICT software and peripherals already in existence to help transform the quality of map work in schools. It is, therefore, disappointing that its use is not more widespread in schools. Map drawing for too many students seems to be little more than a time-consuming activity of drawing and colouring, instead of the technical and thought-provoking activity that it ought to be.

Basic raster mapping

There are many types of drawing programs, most of which can also perform other functions, such as photo manipulation. Programs such as Corel Photo-Paint and Paint Shop Pro have been designed with artwork rather than geography in mind. As such, they contain a wide variety of tools that enable images to be manipulated to produce different artistic effects. For the most part, these effects are not useful for working in geography, and certainly not for drawing maps. This is not to say that these programs cannot be used, but that for the purpose of this section, they probably go beyond what is needed to produce a good basic map. For these basic maps, the MS Paint program has much to offer, even if only as a means of getting started with using a computer to draw maps.

Every PC with the Windows operating system comes with a bundle of programs that includes MS Paint. Consider the tools that it has for drawing maps:

- line drawing to different widths
- colour infill
- an extensive colour palette
- standard shapes, e.g. box and circle
- writing text.

In addition, the user is able to:

- edit the map
- flip, rotate, stretch and skew different shapes
- import a base map from another ICT application, e.g. a website
- view the map in close-up
- save it as a file to be inserted in other ICT applications.

Technique tip

There are many websites and other sources of maps that can be used as a base map for work in Paint. It is best if the base map is a basic clip art graphic without colours. If it does have colours, they may need to be removed so that the map can be used in Paint.

- Basic colours can easily be removed by using the colour infill tool in Paint, replacing the colour with white.
- If the colours are made from combinations of colours – i.e. where combinations of two colours in adjacent pixels are used – you will need to remove the colours by selectively removing each colour with the rubber (erase) tool. This involves a right click to replace one selected colour with white. Check the erase colour procedure in Paint's Help file to see how to do this.

Websites

CIA
Country maps from the CIA's World Factbook are in basic colours from Paint's 24-colour palette. This makes them easy to edit by changing the colour infill to white.

The World Atlas
This website gives the option of both simple outline country maps and maps with basic information, e.g. main cities, rivers and heights.

GenUKI: UK and Ireland Genealogy
A map of counties in Britain that can be used as a base map for mapping in Paint when all counties have been coloured white with the colour infill tool.

Streetmap UK

Teaching idea

Students can draw a map in MS Paint, either from scratch or using an imported base image. This can be a map that uses choropleth shading to show the data. Possible applications might include showing the percentage of households in a town that have more than one car, or the different levels of calorie intake in various countries.

- Open the base image in Paint.
- Draw boundary lines around the areas for which there is raw data, e.g. country boundaries, counties or census areas (it is best if the imported base map already has these boundaries).
- Check that there are no gaps in the boundary lines. If there are, the colour infill will spread outside the area.
- Draw a colour key on the screen, and choose colours for the different categories of data.
- Shade the areas by using the colour infill tool in Paint.
- If the colours do not give an effective visual impression, chose different colours that are better.

Websites

Ordnance Survey: Free & Fun: Outline Maps
A downloadable map of UK counties

Magic
A source of UK maps on regional and national scales for a range of environmental topics, downloadable as PDF files

National Geographic: MapMachine

Graphic Maps
A wide selection of clip art maps

The range of tools in MS Paint is limited, but this is what helps to make it such an easy program for students to use. It does not take much time to teach students how to use it. Besides, even with this range of tools and capabilities, every student can produce maps that are drawn to high technical standards, and in which they can take some pride.

Maps drawn in MS Paint are based on pixels, i.e. the small rectangles that make up the screen. This produces an image that is saved in a raster format. This can, for example, be as a bitmap (.bmp), or in the less space-hungry .jpg and .gif formats. It is essential to know the map format when importing an existing base map into a GIS program.

Anything drawn in MS Paint becomes fixed on the screen, with each pixel only capable of taking one piece of data at a time, e.g. only one colour. This means that layers of data cannot be independently created on the map. One problem with raster images is that individual features are not separately editable – one cannot, for example, click on a shape to move, delete or change its features. The other problem is that the quality of raster maps breaks down into individual pixels as the map is magnified, giving jagged edges to features. Although these are limitations to drawing maps in MS Paint, this program still has a potential role to play in raising standards in drawing maps.

Vector-drawing tools

It may appear odd to include a word processor as an ICT application that can be used for mapping, but it has some tools that can be of use as stepping

Teaching idea

Students can study how some map features are simplified on different scales by comparing a map with a vertical air photo of the same area. This can be for an area of woodland or for any other feature that is shown as an area.

- Insert a vertical air photo into Word.
- Insert an OS 1:50,000 scale map of the same area into Word.
- Use the Freeform drawing tool in Word to draw exactly around the woods (or other feature) shown on the vertical air photo. The area can be shaded with the colour infill tool.
- Compare the area shown on the map with the outline from the vertical air photo to see the extent to which the map has simplified the area.

Websites

Multimap
Maps with vertical air photos

getmapping
Shows maps and air photos that can be purchased.

Technique tip

To use the drawing tools for mapping, choose either the standard shapes such as the rectangle, or the Freeform drawing tool from the AutoShapes menu.

- Click on AutoShapes and Lines, then choose the Freeform tool.
- Draw around the shape.
- Complete the shape as closely as you can.
- You can colour it in using the colour infill tool, or create different line widths, styles and colours using the options for Lines.

stones towards using GIS software. The drawing tools in MS Word are vector-based, i.e. the same as the drawing tools in GIS software. There are lines, areas and points that can be individually edited in ways that are useful for drawing maps. The Freeform shape in the Lines part of the AutoShapes menu gives a flexible drawing tool for drawing any shape. There are also standard

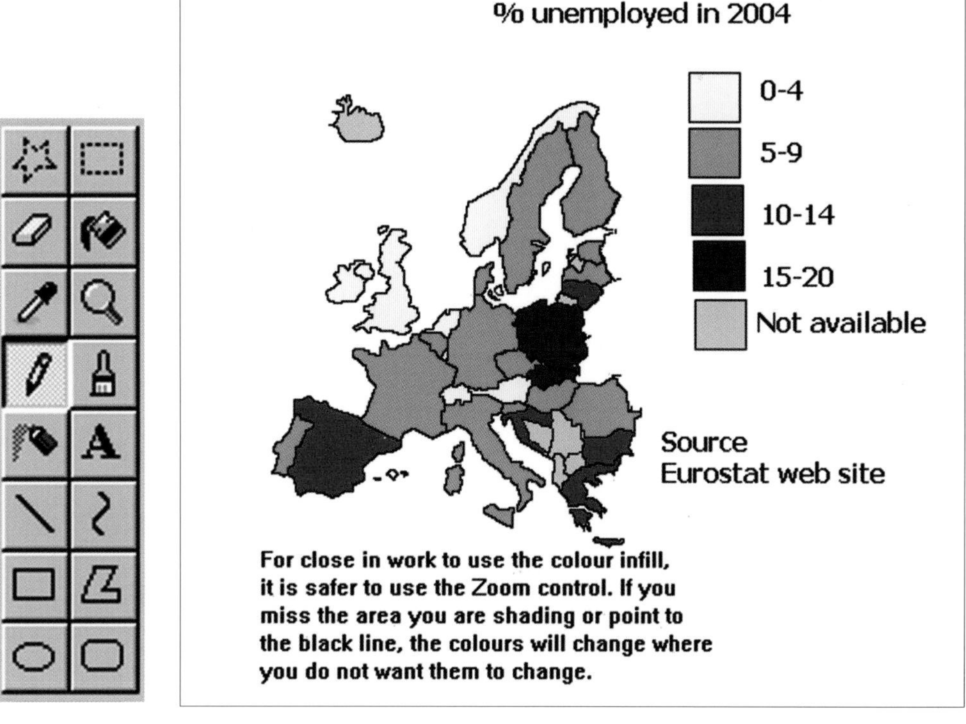

Figure 4.1 *The basic drawing tools in MS Paint can be used to achieve a high technical standard in drawing maps. They have limitations but can still be used effectively to raise the quality of a map or diagram.*

Figure 4.2 *This map has been drawn in MS Paint by importing a clip art outline of Europe, then using the Fill colour tool to show the unemployment levels in the different countries. Four colours have been used on this map, though further categories and colours could easily have been shown. Text can be added and other symbols used. The unemployment data on which the map is based came from the Eurostat website.*

Teaching idea

Students can use a map-drawing program to work on decision-making activities that involve measurements on a map. The Local Studies program is suitable for this activity as it contains a measuring tool. A typical activity might be planning a route for a new road. The route would need to be as short as possible to reduce costs, but should also avoid environmental costs. Line and area measuring tools can be used to work out costs for the different routes.

Website

SoftTeach

Local Studies map-drawing program

shapes such as a straight line, a rectangle and an oval. The rectangle and oval can be used as point symbols for geographic features, and their size can be changed to represent different quantities. Their colour, thickness and position can be changed by clicking on them and then choosing from the Fill Colour, Line Colour and Line Style tools. Control of the mouse to draw a freeform shape, for example, requires considerable practice and a steady hand. It is, however, simple to draw a small symbol such as a circle, then copy and paste it as a standard-sized symbol to any location on the map.

The concept of separate layers of data, which is part of GIS software, can also be demonstrated simply in a word processor. (Layers are also called themes.) This can be done by drawing two or more maps of the same location, each with different types of data (i.e. a different theme). The separate shapes on each map can then be grouped so that they act as one image. The separate maps can then be formatted so that they float over the page. This allows them to be moved over each other in a way that demonstrates how separate map layers can be built up.

Hotspot maps in a word processor

Another way to use a word processor for mapping is to use it to create a virtual field visit. A map can be inserted, then hotspots can be located over it using the drawing tools. Images, text and statistics for each hotspot can be put into the same or a different file, then linked by the hyperlink tool. This is a simple way to illustrate the GIS principle of linking points, areas or lines on a map to other data. It cannot, however, simulate the principle in full, as there is no dynamic link between the two – i.e. the data is not drawn on the map, so the map cannot be changed by changing the data.

Technique tip

The same tools can be used to create hotspots over either a photo or a map:

- Insert a map into Word.
- Insert photos that show places on the map, either into the same Word file or into different Word files.
- Create bookmarks for the photos using the Bookmark tool from the Insert menu.
- Draw rectangles or circles on the map to show where the photos are located.
- Click on the shapes, then hyperlink them to the photos. The link can be to a bookmarked place in the same file, to a different file or to a bookmarked place in a different file.

The hotspots can be made invisible by choosing the No Fill line option from the Fill drawing tool and the No Line option from the Line drawing tool. You have to do this before you create the hyperlink. Students will find the hotspot as they pass the cursor over the shape and the cursor changes to a pointing finger.

Teaching idea

Students can learn how to make appropriate choices of map symbols by using symbols from the AutoShapes in the drawing tools of Word or MS Paint. They can choose symbols that have the following features:

different shapes – choose between rectangle, star, circle and other standard shapes

different sizes – click and drag the shape to a new size

colour – choose from the colour infill and line colour options.

One advantage of using these shapes is that they can be reproduced perfectly each time using a copy and paste procedure. A dot map, for example, can be produced by drawing one dot and then copying it as many times as required. Dots can also be used in different sizes and colours.

Website

Ordnance Survey: Free & Fun

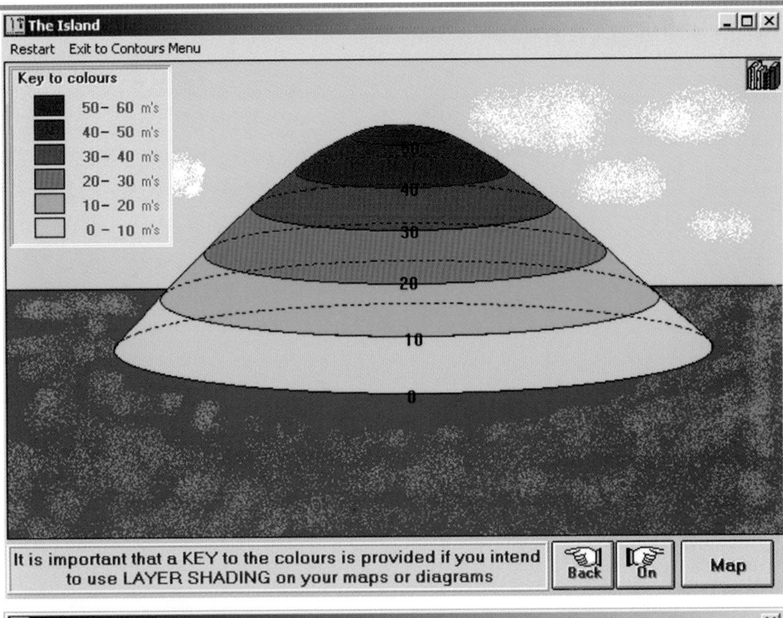

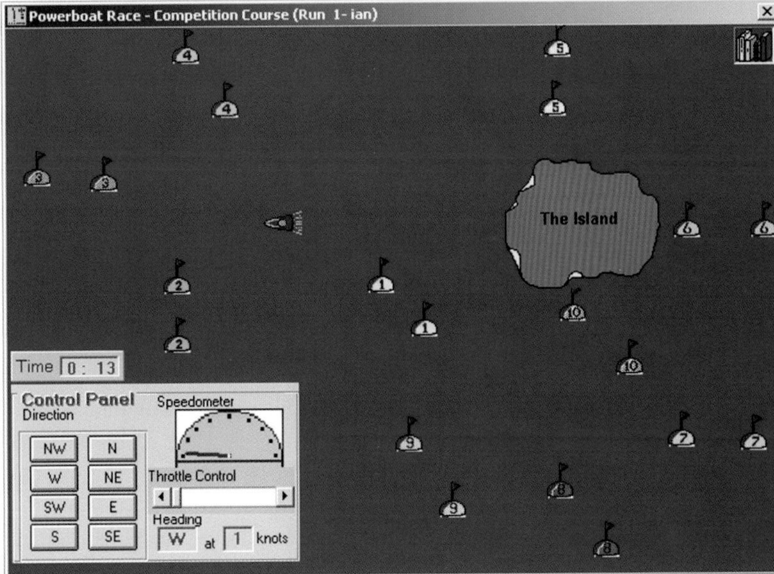

Figure 4.3 *These images show ways in which ICT can be used to create learning games and effective visual images to help engage students in learning about maps. These activities could be done on an interactive whiteboard.*
© Geopacks 08705 133168

Simple map-drawing programs

Some programs have been produced specially for map work in geography. The Local Studies program is an example of one of these. It combines a range of simple drawing tools similar to those in MS Paint with the ability to drag and drop either OS symbols or pictograms. It can also create hotspots that link to photos or digital video clips. Although it does not have tools to map quantitative data linked to a data table, the program can be used to teach some basics of map work. It can also provide a tool for students to draw maps to a good technical standard.

The Mastering Mapwork program was written as an aid to teaching students about maps. It also contains one section in which simple maps can be drawn using the same approach that is used in the Local Studies program, i.e. a combination of basic drawing tools and drag-and-drop symbols. Other parts of the program provide students with opportunities to become familiar with map conventions such as direction, scale and the representation of height. These are presented in a range of imaginative and engaging ways, often with a strong element of game-playing. The program has interesting examples of how ICT tools can be used to simulate the 'hands on' aspect of map work that can be so appealing to kinaesthetic learners. Measuring, for example, is done with a ruler that can be manipulated on screen, while the need for a 3D cardboard model is replaced by animated graphics that simulate a 3D effect.

Making links

NC Orders for Citizenship: KS3 PoS

Developing skills of enquiry and communication

Pupils should be taught to:

- think about topical political, spiritual, moral, social and cultural issues, problems and events by analysing information and its sources, including ICT-based sources
- justify orally and in writing a personal opinion about such issues, problems or events
- contribute to group and exploratory class discussions, and take part in debates.

Web-based maps

There is no problem in obtaining an accurate base map on which data can be mapped in an ICT application. The base map can be at any scale, and may be replaced by a vertical air photo or satellite image. The *Multimap* website, for example, gives UK coverage from national level down to street scale. The maps can be copied and pasted into another application so that quantitative data can be entered over the base layer.

A simple line drawing of every country can be obtained from websites. The Ordnance Survey's *Get-a-map* site offers high-quality maps of the UK at different scales, though unlike the others, this service is only available for an annual subscription. Each department will need to work out the cost of paying for base maps against the likely returns in raising the quality of the students' work in geography.

Outline maps of countries are available on numerous websites, though it can be more difficult to find country maps that have internal boundary lines such as those between census or administrative areas. Some outlines can also be found in interactive whiteboard software – for example, in the map section of the Gallery of the SMART Notebook.

Maps obtained as copies or screen shots from websites are in raster format. This enables them either to be copied into a basic drawing program or to act as a base layer in a GIS program. There are also websites that provide maps in vector format. These can be used in a GIS program.

Maps with tools

Some map programs offer local area data, maps, vertical air photos and satellite images, together with a range of interactive tools. The Digital Worlds and InfoMapper programs are two of these. Maps can be faded over each other, for example, to show how features have changed between an old map

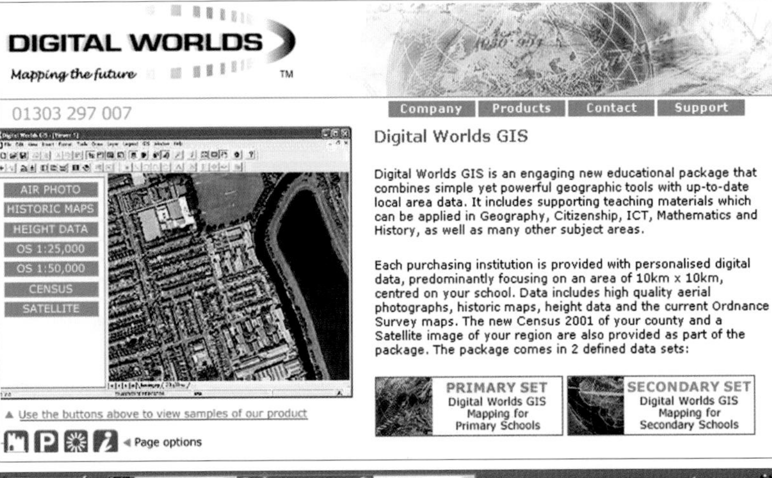

Figure 4.4 *The Digital Worlds map program provides a wealth of map resources for the area around a school. It includes a range of tools with which to view the maps. © Digital Worlds*

Figure 4.5 *The InfoMapper program is a unique mapping resource that provides a range of tools with which to view maps at different scales, vertical air photos and other images. It is a web-based resource for subscribers or by licence though an LEA. © InfoMapper, aerial photography supplied by Bluesky International Ltd*

Teaching idea

Students can use the *Online Map Creation* website to draw a map for any area they are studying. They do this by choosing the latitude and longitude lines for the area and other options. The map is then drawn from the data that has been entered. The map can be saved as a file or copied and pasted into another application, e.g. to use as a base map.

Website

Online Map Creation

and the most recent map. Features such as lines and areas can be measured. Both programs provide students with maps and other images that they can work with in creative and interesting ways – for example, to study issues in local land use or simply to learn more about how to interpret maps, vertical air photos and satellite images. The InfoMapper program allows students to download their work onto a website. This enables students in different schools to see what others are doing.

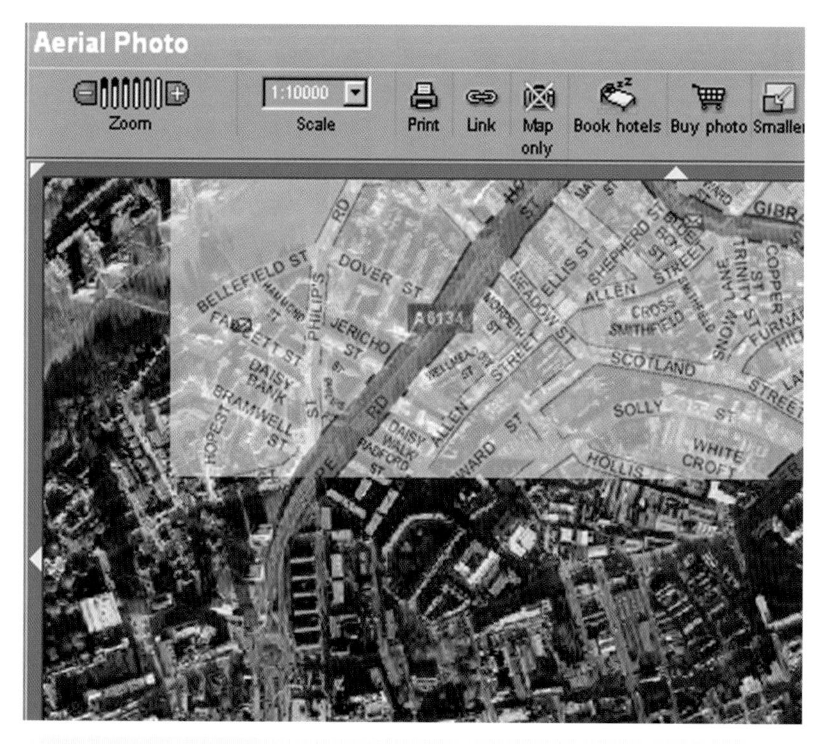

Figure 4.6 *The* Multimap *website has several useful tools and functions, including the ability to move a transparent map over a vertical air photo so that street patterns can be seen and names can be read. Source: Getmapping*

Teaching idea

The *Multimap* website has a tool that can be used to show how a vertical air photo relates to a map. This tool creates a square in which a ghost image of a map can be passed over the vertical air photo. This is a useful tool for helping students develop both their map-reading and photo interpretation skills. There is a similar tool in the Aegis 3, Digital Worlds and InfoMapper programs.

Websites
Multimap
Digital Worlds
InfoMapper

Teaching idea

Multimap and some other map websites can be used to demonstrate the effects of changing the scale on a map. These websites have Zoom (enlarge) and Reduce tools that change the scale of the map area. They also change the type of map, selecting out different levels of detail as appropriate. In *Multimap*, note how the 1:50000 scale maps are used at two different scales, simply by enlarging the map to show a smaller area but to a different size. In all other respects the map stays the same, i.e. in the detail, symbols and exactly what is shown. This is a complexity of scale that students using these maps would need to understand.

Teaching idea

Use the SMART Notebook to create a map of a continent with country outlines as a background. Place the outlines for individual countries on the page. Different things can be done with the outlines, such as locating them on the background map. To make it more difficult, the individual country outlines can be rotated. The most difficult activity is to place the country outlines on the screen without a background of the continent and countries, or with the country boundaries painted over so they cannot be seen.

Landscape rendering

Landscape rendering is a way of changing a map landscape to one that has the effect of photo-realism. This means converting it to a 3D effect and colouring its surface to make it look as much like a photo as possible. Additional features can then be added as shapes that stand up, such as buildings, trees and wind turbines. The Genesis II program can be used to do this. Although it has been set up to work with areas that measure 7 km by 7 km, it can be used selectively for work on areas with different dimensions.

A first step in using the program is to create a landscape with height data. There are different ways to do this:

- plotting spot heights on a blank map
- drawing contours on a blank map
- importing a background map with contours, and drawing either spot heights or contours over the map
- using an autotrace tool that copies contour lines automatically
- importing a Digital Terrain map with heights incorporated in digital form.

Once the base map with heights has been completed, the program can convert the map into a 3D effect. It can do this so that a smooth landscape is achieved, even with a limited input of height data – though more data does give a better map. The viewing angle and direction can be changed by repositioning the camera angle. This allows the 2D map to be shown from any viewpoint as a 3D image. The link between contours, heights and landform shape become immediately clear, in the same way as can be achieved by building a cardboard relief model.

The program then takes mapping on to a different dimension. It has a range of tools that allow the landscape to be rendered, showing areas of vegetation, buildings, roads and other features. The appearance of the sky can be changed, and selections made as to the angle of the sun and the time of year. Snow can be shown on the higher slopes in winter, or an autumn landscape can be chosen. Land can be flooded with water – perhaps a useful way to simulate how global warming may cause a rise in sea level. The ability of the program to work with 'what if' scenarios is dealt with in Chapter 7.

Teaching idea

One use of the Genesis II program is to help students understand how contour shapes show height. It does this by converting a map with contour or spot height data into a 3D image. The image can be viewed from any angle. Landscapes can also be made to look realistic by using the rendering tools.

Websites

Geomantics
The Genesis II program is available as a free download or the full version may be purchased.

Ordnance Survey
Using Genesis with students

Ordnance Survey
Fly-through animations that link contours to 3D effects in an animation

memory-map
Map-making software

Technique tip

Students can use Excel to draw 3D landscape diagrams. This technique is described and illustrated in detail in the geography section of the Wycombe High School website:

- Enter height data into a spreadsheet on a grid of, for example, 10 rows and columns. Include figures or letters for the grid in column A and row A.
- Choose the Surface graphs and the sub-type 3D Surface option.
- When the graph has been drawn, students can rotate it to show the diagram from different angles.
- The height of the land can be coloured using the editing tools for the format of the graph.
- The scale height of the diagram can be adjusted in the 3D view option – for example, reducing the default scaling from 100% to 25%.

Website

Wycombe High School

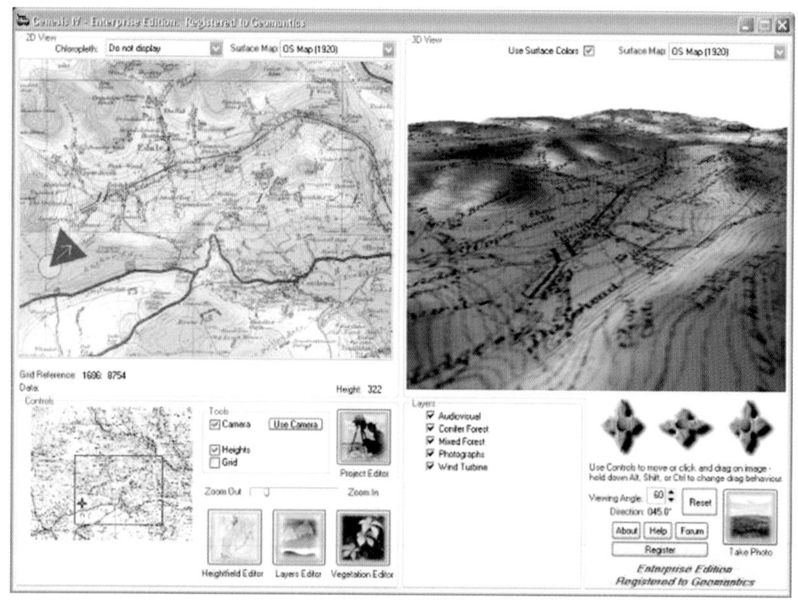

Figure 4.7 *Landscape rendering is a way of creating a photo-realistic landscape from a map. The Genesis II program combines the ability to map a landscape with showing what it looks like in 3D. The appearance of the landscape can be changed to show different types of vegetation, and new features can be added to the landscape.*

An alternative or complementary method of landscape rendering is to drape a vertical air photo over the base map. When converted to 3D effect, the landscape is then shown with the photo-realism of the vertical air photo, showing fields, roads and buildings in their correct rather than their simulated colours.

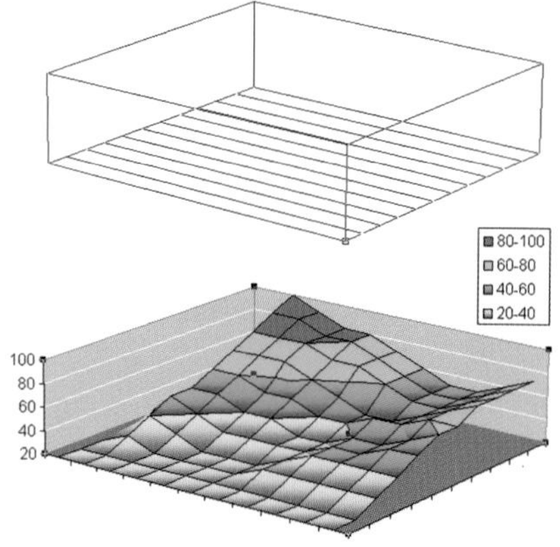

Figure 4.8 *The Excel spreadsheet program can be used to create 3D landscapes by entering height data into cells. The landscape can be coloured into layers to simulate different types of land use. The image can then be rotated and viewed from any angle.*

GIS software

Geographic Information Systems (GIS) provides geographers with what is currently the ultimate mapping tool. There are industry-standard programs such as ArcView and MapInfo, as well as programs that were written for use in schools. Of the latter, Aegis 3 is probably the best known and the most used. What is surprising is that so few schools are making use of GIS software – surprising because it is the only ICT application that has been designed to do what geographers want to do, i.e. show patterns of spatial data.

The basic features of GIS software are that it can be used:

- to draw accurate maps at any scale
- to edit map details such as outlines and shapes
- to show layers (themes) of features, either together or selected
- to link raw data to points, areas and lines on the map
- to link the raw data dynamically to the map so that changes to the data table are shown in how the data is mapped
- to map the raw data in a variety of styles
- to process, search and query map data.

Accurate maps can be created by:

- drawing from scratch using vector-based tools to draw points, lines and areas (polygons)
- importing a raster image as a base map, which can be a map, a vertical air photo or a satellite image
- importing a vector-based map, e.g. an OS map in .ntf format.

Each point, line and area on the map must be given a map code. This allows the feature to be identified and linked to raw data in a data base. Each type of feature can be draw as a separate layer – for example, one layer can represent buildings, another roads and another fields.

Making links

NC Orders for ICT: Attainment Targets, Level 7

Pupils combine information from a variety of ICT-based and other sources for presentation to different audiences. They identify the advantages and limitations of different information-handling applications. They select and use information systems suited to their work in a variety of contexts, translating enquiries expressed in ordinary language into the form required by the system.
Note how mapping software could be interpreted as a form of presentation and as a type of information handling system.

Base stations in Andover

Click on the map before choosing the data to map on it.
Enlarge the maps to show greater detail.
Use the map layer control (in Map) to show different types of map data.

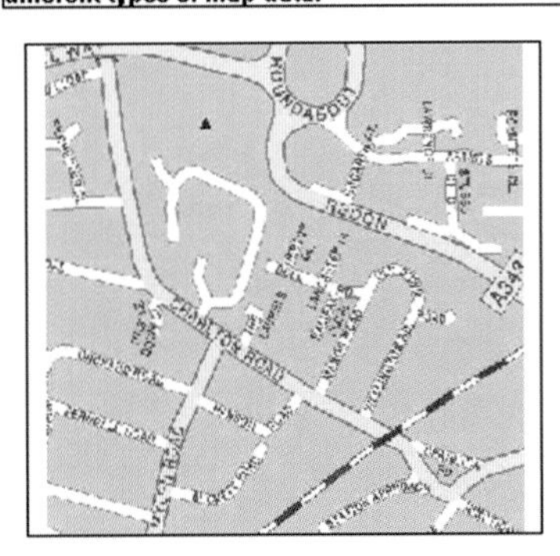

Location of base stations - above
Click on the red squares on the map below to show the locations.

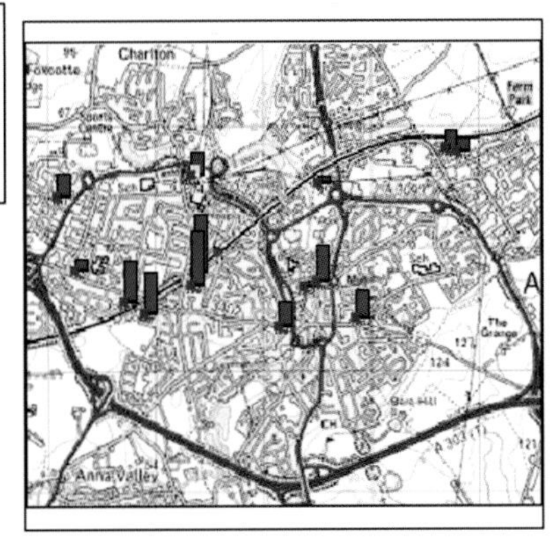

Base station data map -left
Data table - below

	Base	Height	Power	Range
1	m1	15.0	26.40	1800.0
2	m2	7.0	28.00	1800.0
3	m3	26.0	25.50	2100.0
4	m4	26.0	25.50	2100.0
5	m5	37.0	27.00	1800.0
6	m6	35.0	25.50	900.0

Figure 4.9 *This image shows how a map with data and images can be shown in the Aegis 3 GIS program. The map shows the location and heights of base stations (mobile phone masts) in Andover. The data comes from the* Ofcom Sitefinder *website*

Raw data is collected, either as words or preferably as numeric data, the latter being more easily mapped using quantitative mapping styles. The data is entered on a table in much the same way as a database is created. Each row represents a record of data for the point, line or area. There may, for example, be different items of data about a building, such as its height, the number of people who enter it over time, its functions and its value. These items of data represent the data fields in the database. The essential factor in making the map work is ensuring that the record in the data table contains the same code as has been given to the point, line or area on the map.

The result is a map that can be drawn to show the data in a variety of ways, making choices as to the map style that is appropriate to the data and what the map is intended to show. Area data can be mapped as bars, choropleth shading, proportional pies or in other styles. The style of mapping can be adjusted by choosing different colours, data categories or in other ways. Even students who have problems with drawing neatly by hand are able to produce high-quality maps. Although data shown in a particular map style can be saved, the style of map is essentially transient. The same data can be mapped in different ways to suit different purposes by choosing different mapping options. The program generates the map instantly, so there is no need to save anything except the map themes and the data tables for each theme.

Teaching idea

Carry out an enquiry into a local area topic for which numeric data can be collected for lines, areas or points. The topic chosen might include such aspects as patterns of local crime, local traffic flows, provision of shops and services, or the use of recreation spaces.

- Use a GIS program as a means of recording data and of mapping it in different ways; set up different fields (themes) of relevant data.
- Look at the maps and query the map data to find patterns.
- Use the maps to see if any of the data seems to be related or if there are any processes that link the data.

Websites

Royal Geographical Society: Getting Started with GIS
BECTA: Introduction to GIS
ESRI (UK)
ESRI
Suppliers of ArcView GIS program, with sample lessons using ArcView
The Advisory Unit: Computers in Education
Aegis 3 GIS program with sample ideas for enquiries
VDS Technologies
Website with vector map downloads for use in a GIS program
Kingston Centre for GIS
USGS: Global GIS Curriculum
Ofcom Sitefinder
Ordnance Survey: GIS files

Teaching idea

The OS Survey CD-Rom has a tool for choosing different layers of map data for the same area. This is done by switching the layers of data on or off. Doing this should help the students to understand how data for a map needs to be selected and how links between data can sometimes be identified visually.

Teaching idea

The ArcVoyager Special Edition GIS program has a tool that allows the user to change the map projection for world maps. It also lets the user rotate the globe in any direction. This can be useful in helping students develop a better understanding of:

- how the shapes and areas of countries and continents are shown differently in different map projections
- how perceptions of the distances between places and the routes between them can be changed by using different map projections
- how different the world can look when seen from a different central point, e.g. when centred on another country (the Pacific 'ring of fire' is best seen from a map centred on Hawaii).

Teaching idea

OS Digital maps (called Land-Line maps) for all parts of England are available to schools through the LEA. The maps for the local area are provided free of charge to all state schools and to other schools for a fee. Some LEAs levy a nominal handling charge.

- The maps can be inserted as accurate base maps into a GIS program.
- They contain many layers of map data that can be switched on or off.
- They are vector-based, so they can be enlarged without loss of quality.
- The students can draw new layers with their own research data over these base maps.

Although other ICT applications can be used to map data, only GIS software has the ability to process, search and query it in order to answer specific questions. This is done in the same way as setting up a query in a data base – for example, by identifying and then mapping only those places that have a population total above or below a given figure. Areas and distances can be calculated instantly. This can help in answering questions about, for example, the number of people who would be living within 100 metres of a new road if one were to be built through the area.

Vertical air photos

Vertical air photos are now part of an integrated system of resources that can show the spatial distribution of data. They can be used, either on their own as a base map for GIS or other map work, or alongside maps to help with map interpretation. Sometimes it is the map that helps in the interpretation of the

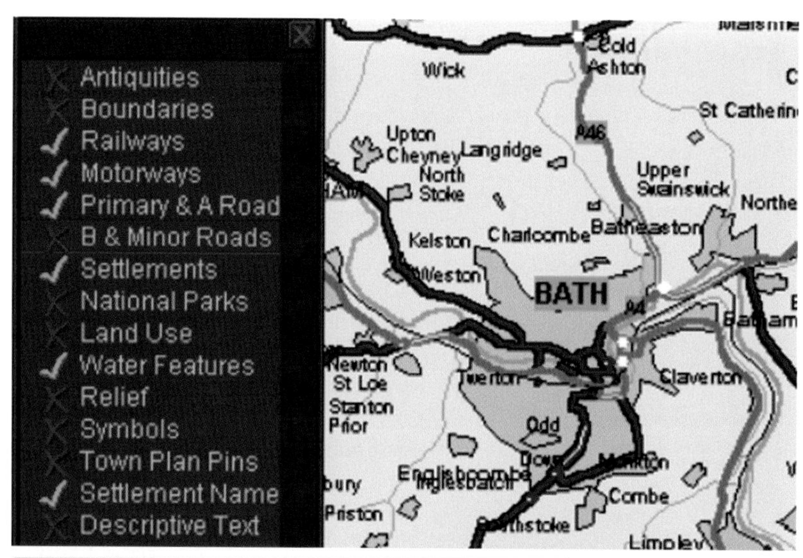

Figure 4.10 *The OS Survey CD-Rom has layers of data that can be switched on or off in the same way as choosing themes (layers) in a GIS program. Maps could be captured and shown side by side, or layers could be shown on the same map. © Crown Copyright Ordnance Survey*

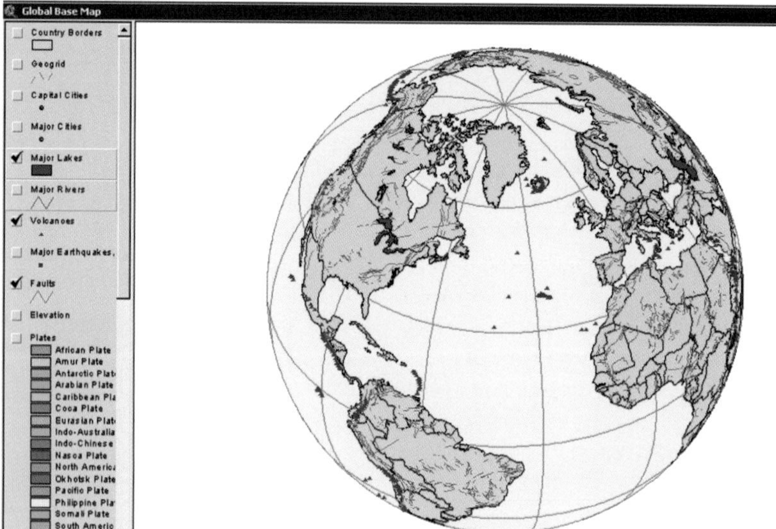

Figure 4.11 *ICT can be used to draw a map from selected data. This image shows the ArcVoyager GIS program. This is a lite version of the ArcView GIS program. Students can get a visual correlation of map themes by choosing to show different variables on the same map. Provided courtesy of ESRI (UK)*

photo, using a split-screen effect to show both at the same time. Points on the photo can also be geo-referenced so that it can be draped over the map. This can be done to show a 3D photo-realistic landscape. Although there are several websites from which vertical air photos can be downloaded, their quality is poor when compared to a high-quality print (which can be expensive). However, poorer-quality web-based vertical air photos are still useful for many types of work in geography.

Satellite imagery

Satellite imagery represents a special type of map. The data that makes up a satellite image is captured in digital form by remote sensing – for example, from the Landsat or SPOT orbiting satellites. Data is captured in different

Teaching idea

Use vertical air photos to draw land use maps for an area. One way to do this is to import the air photo into MS Paint, then to use the Drawing and Fill colour tools to create a simplified set of shapes to show different types of land use. Remember, however, that the background image cannot be removed in Paint. It is only possible to hide it by filling in a colour over it.

Websites

Multimap

Maps and vertical air photos for the UK

TerraServer-USA

Vertical air photos of the USA

wavelengths from different parts of the electromagnetic spectrum. It is then selectively combined and processed to create visual images. If satellite images are taken at a sufficiently high resolution and processed with appropriate colours, they can be made to look like vertical air photos. There are different ways of capturing the data – for example, by using radar or by recording reflected heat. Both visible and invisible parts of the electromagnetic spectrum are used, as some types of data can be more easily detected in different ways. The mid-infra-red band, for example, is an effective band from which to collect data about moisture content in soil. Radar images can be used to collect height data irrespective of cloud conditions.

ICT applications for processing satellite imagery are currently little, if ever, used in schools. Images in different bands are available, for example, as weather data, but students in schools do not have the opportunity to develop the skills to process the data themselves. Perhaps if they did, they would be able to develop a better understanding of what the images show.

Zooming in

The *Google Earth* website and program is worth a special mention as it combines several features of mapping into one interactive resource. It has a search facility that can find places in any country, often down to quite small settlements. The resource uses a combination of real-colour satellite images and what appear to be vertical air photos, allowing the user to zoom in from a whole-earth image to large-scale levels of detail. It is very much a case of looking at the places through the geographer's 'lens'. Layers of data can be switched on or off – for example, schools, airports, roads and volcanoes. The data is streamed through from a website, the speed depending on the processing power of the computer. The program can also show the landscape in 3D with a fly-through tool. One can, for example, follow a route through the Swiss Alps, along a motorway or river, or any other place on earth.

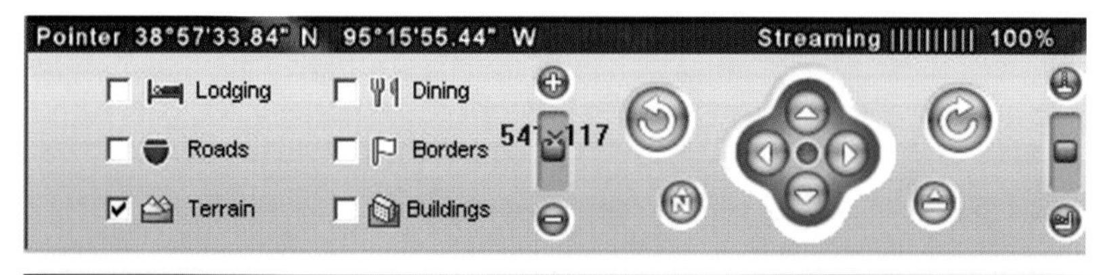

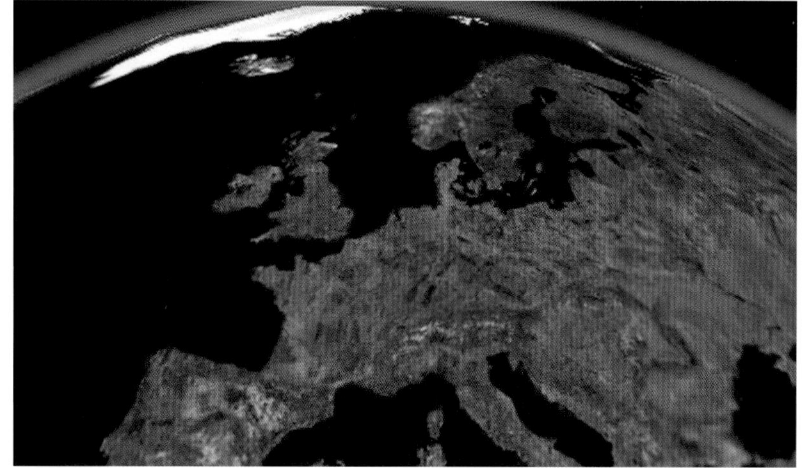

Figure 4.12 *Screen shots from the Google Earth program. The earth is shown on satellite images at air photo quality with the ability to fly through a 3D landscape. Different layers of data can be switched on or off.*

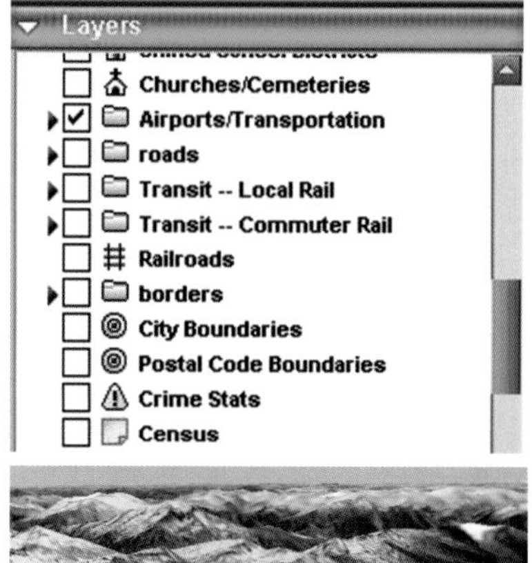

Teaching idea

Look at some satellite images that show the same area using different bands. Make links to the students' work in science to explain how the images have been captured using different wavelengths in the electromagnetic spectrum. Develop the students' understanding of false colours and why they are used for satellite images. The *Window on the World* CD-Rom is one source of satellite images and how they can be both used and interpreted. This CD is available from the BNSC website.

Website

BNSC

This website about the uses of space technology is a source of the free CD-Roms *Window on the World* and *Window on the UK2000.*

Teaching idea

Introduce students to the idea of false colour on satellite images by providing some images from websites or other sources.

- Locate the images on atlas maps.
- Read descriptions of what the images show.
- Work out a colour key for the images.
- Present ideas on how the image could help solve a land use problem.

Websites

USGS: Earthshots

Landsat.org

NASA

Teaching idea

Use the Google Earth program to find out about land use under the flight paths that lead to the main runway at Birmingham Airport. You can find the airport by using the Search tool, then simulate an approach to the runway by flying towards it, increasing the scale and changing the angle of viewing. The coverage for this area is of higher quality than a vertical air photo, so you will be able to identify different types of buildings and open space. Think about the types of land use that would be compatible with aircraft noise and safety, and see if the flight paths to Birmingham Airport might cause any problems.

Websites

Google Earth

NewsGlobe

News events on Google Earth

Teaching idea

Look at satellite images for the weather over the UK on the *Dundee Satellite Receiving Station* website. Look both at the visible and some of the infra-red images. As a simple principle, the areas with the clearest white are where the cloud is deepest. On the infra-red images, the coldest areas show as the whitest, i.e. the highest layers of cloud. Use this principle to work out the types of cloud and the weather patterns for the area shown on the image. Students can also look at the pseudo-colour image to see how this is different.

Website

Dundee Satellite Receiving Station

University of Dundee's satellite receiving station for polar-orbiting weather satellite images – free registration for access to the latest images.

Wider issues relating to mapping with ICT

Drawing maps and processing map data with the use of ICT opens up enormous opportunities for raising the standard of mapping. It also opens up a range of issues relating to the criteria for assessing map work and defining the standards that geography teachers should expect their students to achieve. Exploring these issues may raise more questions than it provides answers, but they are issues that will need to be resolved as the use of ICT continues to gain momentum in schools.

Technical proficiency

It is difficult to argue against the assertion that the technical quality of computer-drawn maps will always be better than that of maps drawn by hand. In all the criteria set out for defining high standards in drawing a map, the use of ICT has clear advantages. For processing map data, the use of ICT will always be the most efficient and the most accurate method. Although there are other aspects of map work to consider, the tools for producing better-quality maps are all available using ICT.

Choosing and using the appropriate map-drawing tools is a different question, though of course a student could equally choose and use inappropriate hand-drawn methods. It is more difficult to use a mouse and cursor to draw a freeform line than to draw by hand, though practice can achieve first-rate results and there are other ways to create digital freeform lines than by using a mouse and cursor. At least it is easier to edit, or completely remove, lines drawn on a computer, compared to the problems involved in rubbing out lines drawn on paper. Drawing curved shapes by means of vector-based graphics is especially difficult. They have to be made from combinations of short straight lines, though even vector-based lines can be bent using editing tools in some drawing and mapping programs.

In the area of colours, text, signs and symbols, the use of ICT is the most effective way to create graphics of high-quality technical uniformity. The range of colours in a drawing program's basic colour palette will provide more than enough colours for the purposes of mapping. The task of locating text on a map is made easy by tools that can drag and drop text in any position, rotating it if necessary. Map clutter can be avoided by using GIS software, as this enables different layers to be switched on or off as required.

Decisions in mapping

Although the present focus is on the technical skill of drawing maps, it is obvious that a map cannot be drawn without making decisions based on an understanding of their conventions and techniques. The use of ICT largely removes the need for technical ability, unless one counts the ability to use a program's drawing tools as a form of technical ability. Instead, what ICT offers to map drawing is a wide range of choices regarding the overall appearance and the styles that can be used to map the data. A parallel can be drawn with the way in which the use of a spreadsheet opens up new choices in the style of graph that can be drawn.

Because, however, there are now so many choices in terms of colour, fonts and presentation of quantitative data, students need to be taught the characteristics of these options and how to make appropriate choices. This presents a new challenge for geography teachers, especially with students for whom such a choice has never previously been available. Drawing the map is no longer the problem. The focus instead needs to be on students developing a much deeper and more finely honed understanding as to the visual impact of what they have drawn. Spending time doing this must surely help to raise standards in mapping.

The use of ICT also makes it easy to experiment with different choices. Changing the range of colours used in a key takes no longer than typing in the commands. Editing any part of the map can be done with equal ease, whether changing shapes, data, text or any other feature.

Issues of progression

It is interesting to speculate on how ideas about progression in map drawing apply to working with ICT. There is no longer any gradation in its technical appearance. In mapping by hand, there can be progression in how the lines, fonts, shading and other features are drawn, whereas the same is not true for maps produced by using ICT. Everything is produced to the same technical perfection every time. Progression, therefore, will need to be sought in other aspects of the work. This may be in how well the map is designed, the choice of content and how the map data is shown. Progression may also include the extent to which the map data can be processed – i.e. the extent to which one can interact with it. The boundary line that separates drawing the map from processing the data no longer seems valid.

Developing map-drawing skills

It is reasonable to make sure that students in their early years are able to draw at least some features of a map by hand. This can extend to drawing quantitative symbols and locating them in appropriate places. But once this has been achieved, it is then questionable as to whether there is any further need to keep repeating the same kind of basic activity when ICT offers an alternative that produces better and faster results. An accurate base map of a country can easily be imported, either from a website or as clip art from a CD-Rom. The most accurate OS base maps of landscape features and terrain can also be imported. This allows more time to be spent on the more important task of mapping the data. When even that can be done using ICT, one must question whether a point should be reached when one should expect maps to be drawn using ICT. It is difficult to identify a precise age, year or key stage when this should happen, though for many students the use of ICT for drawing maps should be the norm by at least KS4. This is not to say that the use of ICT for drawing maps should begin at KS4. There is certainly no reason why it cannot begin when students are first introduced to maps. MS Paint can be an effective tool for drawing basic maps, and the use of this program is well within the capabilities of relatively young students.

Something lost

Some teachers may question whether the use of ICT for drawing maps will mean that something is lost. Inevitably, this will be the case. The traditional cartographer's skill in drawing maps by hand, adding occasional personal touches to create a unique style, may be a victim of change. One response to this is that there will still be some need, no matter how limited, for maps to be drawn that have a more personal and artistic style, though only for special purposes. Producers of advertising material, for example, may choose to use such a style in an attempt to create a particular image of a place. This, however, becomes the field for artists and graphic designers, not for geographers.

It can also be argued that students will not develop the same understanding of maps if they do not draw them by hand. They may not, for example, learn the shape of countries so easily if they always use clip art. This is probably a valid argument, though the strength of this argument depends on how important one thinks it is for students to be able to draw an outline by hand or to know a shape from memory. This is a discussion that can rapidly degenerate into the old argument over the relative importance of knowledge against the ability to find out. One final point is to reflect on the value of what is gained, relative to what might be lost.

Integrating images

Although most of the comments in this section refer to maps, the use of ICT has meant that other types of images have also become important. In particular, vertical air photos and satellite images have now become an accepted part of the geographer's tool kit. Since ICT is able to handle all forms of digital resource with equal ease, the interchange and integration of different types of resources is not a problem. A vertical air photo, for example, can be imported to act as a base map in a GIS program. The same is true for a satellite image. By fading one image, it is even possible to ghost one image over another so that street names can be read from an underlying vertical air photo.

This widening of the definition of mapping would appear to call for a greater degree of thinking about vertical air photos and satellite images. While a considerable amount of time is usually spent in learning about mapping, there is a dearth of information in school geography textbooks on the conventions and processes that relate to either vertical air photo or satellite images. There is a case to be made for developing the students' knowledge and understanding of how vertical air photo stereo images are taken and how they can be used. A similar argument can be made for satellite images, even if this involves making reference to the science behind them. Until this is done, students in geography will not be able to do anything with either vertical air photos or satellite images, other than use them as surrogate maps without sufficient understanding to interpret them properly.

The argument for GIS

The use of GIS cannot be anything other than 'good' geography. It could, of course, be used to create 'bad' geography if the data it presents is faulty or the maps it produces are misinterpreted, but this can apply to maps drawn in any kind of way. If used properly, GIS can bring together all the advantages of using ICT for drawing maps and processing map data into one package.

The fact that GIS has become such a standard tool in so many different types of employment adds further mystery to why school geography departments have been so slow to take it up. There are, of course, several reasons to explain this. The most often stated reasons are to do with:

- the lack of teacher training in GIS work
- the cost of GIS software
- the relative complexity of GIS programs
- the time required to ensure that students become confident users
- the general problems of access to computer rooms, making it difficult to justify the cost and time that working with GIS is perceived to require
- the fact that there is no compulsion in National Curriculum or exam board criteria to ensure that geography students become confident users of GIS.

It would be sad if geographers waited until forced into using GIS by changes to the National Curriculum Orders for Geography or exam board regulations. Even the present cohort of undergraduates is not guaranteed access to GIS work as part of their geography degree. It could certainly be argued that any degree that carried the title 'geography' should regard work with GIS as a central component of its work, irrespective of whichever other modules are studied. For a subject that claims to have 'real world' credentials, this is a situation that has to be rectified.

Learning to use GIS software is not easy. It performs so many functions that it is bound to be complex. But it would be a mistake to leave its use until the students are older – for example, until they reach KS4 or even KS5. Because it is not easy, the logic ought to be that the students should start to use it earlier, not later! Its separate components can be easily identified, such as the ability to draw shapes with vector-based graphics and the ability to work with a database. These components can be individually taught from the early years, and certainly from no later than year 7 in KS3. If a step-by-step approach is adopted, and the program is regularly used, students should get to where they need to be by KS4. By then, they should already be able to make constructive use of the maps they have drawn, rather than having to spend time starting to learn how to use the program's tools. As an alternative to the step-by-step approach, a 'big bang' approach to teaching a GIS program can also work. This involves getting students to work with the program for a concentrated period of hours over a limited number of days. It is, of course, then necessary to ensure that they continue to use the program for mapping activities in the context of different topics.

Assessing maps drawn using ICT

Numerous references have already been made to the issues surrounding the assessment of maps that have been drawn using ICT. Some of these issues are the same as for other types of work that have been produced with ICT, such as drawing graphs or research. But for drawing maps, these issues are even greater. This is because the quality of maps is so much improved by the use of ICT compared with maps drawn by hand. There are also so many additional functions that can be performed and that it would simply not be realistic to do in any other way.

Neatness, accuracy and an appropriate choice of mapping styles should be of key importance in the success criteria for drawing maps. It may be argued that it is simply not fair to compare maps drawn with ICT with maps drawn by hand, and that different criteria ought to apply to each. This position, however, is not tenable. As was argued towards the beginning of this chapter, the criteria must apply to the end result, not the process that has been used to get there. It is surely up to the teachers to make sure that their students are not put at a disadvantage by not having access to the right hardware and software. This is one issue for further thought.

Teaching idea

Make a study of the shopping centre of Stourbridge by using the interactive map on the website (below) and other sources of information.

- What is the general size and layout of the shopping centre?
- What is the population total of Stourbridge and the surrounding area?
- Where are the next nearest shopping centres to Stourbridge?
- How do the shops and services rank in a hierarchy of shopping centres?
- What is the balance of shops to services?
- How does the Stourbridge shopping centre compare with one near to where you live?

Website

Stourbridge

An interactive map of the town's shopping centre

Chapter 5 Working with data

Key questions

- What are the links between work in geography and both the NC Orders for ICT and the Secondary (KS3) Strategy for mathematics?
- What are the characteristics of high-quality working with data in geography?
- Which ICT applications can be used to handle geographic data, i.e. to record, present and process it?
- What are the advantages of using ICT for data handling?
- What are the issues in teaching and learning that arise when ICT is used in data handling?

ICT applications

- Spreadsheet
- Database

Focus on data handling

Raw data provides geographers with the evidence for carrying out enquiries, whether from primary or secondary research. The focus in this chapter is on handling numeric data. Although this is usually in the form of quantitative data, even qualitative data can often be given a numeric value through the use of an index. The particular focus is on what is usually called 'data handling'. This mainly relates to how data is recorded, presented and processed, i.e. the stages before it is analysed and interpreted to give meaningful information and lead to conclusions.

The recording, processing and presentation of data is important to carrying out an enquiry, though it is a means to an end rather than the focus for the enquiry. One problem with data handling can be the inordinate amount of time that it takes to process and present it, especially if one is aiming for statistical reliability. The use of a calculator can speed up some of these functions. The use of ICT will not only achieve greater speed, but will also provide a wide range of options for both statistical calculations and the visual representation of data as graphs. The main types of ICT applications that can do this are spreadsheets and databases. These may be generic programs such as Excel or Access, or ones that have been written specially for work in geography. Presenting data is usually regarded as a geographical skill – for example, in the NC Orders for Geography and in exam board assessment criteria. One could argue that there is nothing especially geographical in presenting data as graphs, but working with quantitative data on maps is a more specialist activity in geography. Perhaps one way to think about handling data in geography is as part of a wider concern with using visual methods to present it. The focus, therefore, should be not so much on the technical ability to draw

Making links

NC Orders for ICT: KS3 PoS

Developing ideas and making things happen

Pupils should be taught:

- to develop and explore information, solve problems and derive new information for particular purposes [for example, deriving totals from raw data, reaching conclusions by exploring information].

Making links

KS3 Strategy: Mathematics

Numeracy is a proficiency which is developed mainly in mathematics but also in other subjects.
Poor numeracy skills hold back pupils' progress and can lower their self-esteem. Improving these skills is a whole-school matter. Each department should identify the contribution it makes towards numeracy skills so that pupils become confident at tackling mathematics in any context.

Websites

The Standards Site: Mathematics Framework: Numeracy and Mathematics

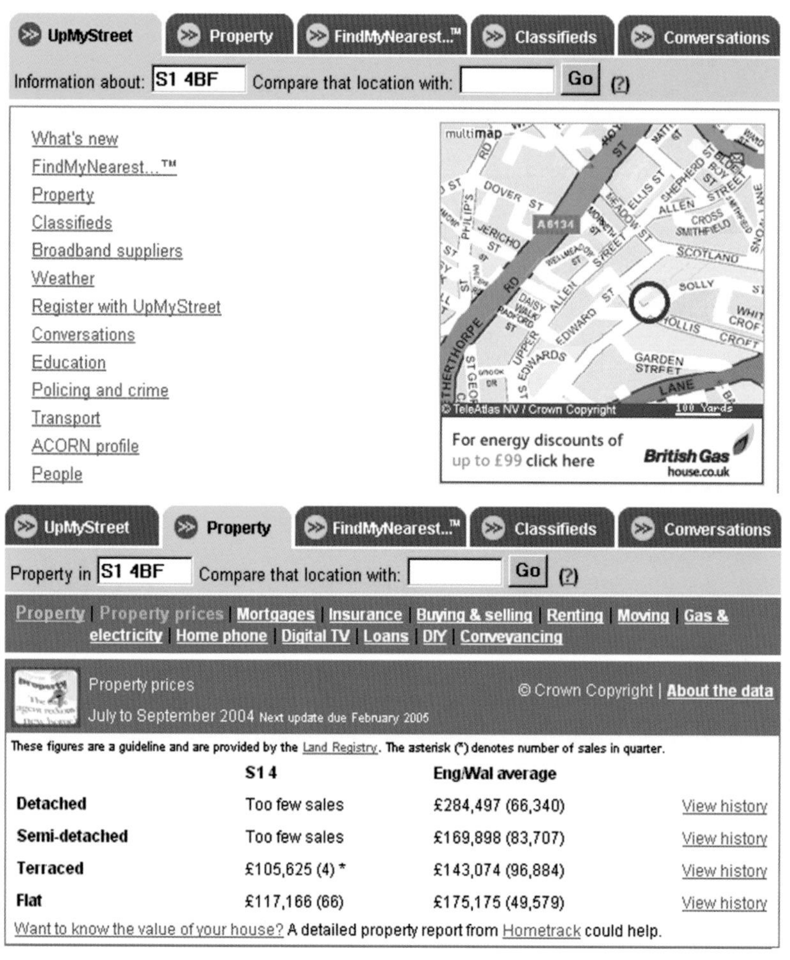

Figure 5.1 *Local area data can be searched on several websites by entering a postcode. The* UpMyStreet *website gives figures about the local area that can be compared with those for other areas and with national data.*

> ### Making links
> ***NC Orders for Geography: KS3 PoS***
>
> ***Geographical enquiry and skills***
> In undertaking geographical enquiry, pupils should be taught to:
> - collect, record and present evidence [for example, statistical information about countries, data about river channel characteristics

> ### Making links
> ***Key Stage 3 National Strategy ICT across the curriculum: ICT in geography***
>
> ***Using data and information sources***
> There is a wealth of information and up-to-date statistics on websites, giving access to material relevant to geographical enquiry that simply could not be available through any other medium. Pupils have unparalleled opportunities to identify, select and use sources appropriate to particular enquiries. The quantity of material available on the internet gives pupils opportunities to develop skills that help them to evaluate both the information they receive and the websites themselves.

the map or graph, but on making appropriate choices as to which technique would suit the purpose for which the data has been collected and is being presented. As with so many things in geography, this involves taking a wider view of the work. This wider view may involve the need to integrate text, maps, diagrams and other illustrations in ways that allow a geographical enquiry to be presented in the most effective manner.

Geographical quality in data handling

A definition of high-quality data handling in geography can be considered in several contexts:

- data in descriptions written as text
- data in maps and graphs
- data for calculations.

Incorporating data into descriptions helps add detail to the descriptions by taking the subjective quality out of adjectives such as big, small, high, low,

> ## Making links
> ***NC Orders: Thinking Skills***
>
> Information-processing skills enable pupils to:
> - locate, collect and recall relevant information
> - interpret information to show they understand relevant concepts and ideas
> - analyse information, e.g. sort, classify, sequence, compare and contrast
> - understand relationships, e.g. part/whole relationships.
>
> Enquiry skills enable pupils to:
> - plan what to do and how to research
> - predict outcomes, test conclusions and improve ideas.

near or far. For example, if one uses figures for altitude and slope angle as part of a description of the relief and landforms of a landscape, this can make the description more technical and meaningful. It is also important for data to be presented in visually accessible ways when drawing maps and graphs. Making calculations is another way to make data meaningful – for example, by identifying trends, testing for relationships and making predictions. Whatever the context, there are some characteristics of the data, and some aspects of how it is handled, that should identify it as being good-quality geography.

TABLE UV02 POPULATION DENSITY (South West only) ▶ **Footnotes** ▶ **About**

Report file format: -- Select file format -- Download

Data may be unavailable for some high area levels (e.g. United Kingdom or Great Britain).
To view statistics for lower area levels, click on the area name displayed in the table.

▼ Next (Rows 1-25 of 35)

Variables / Area	ALL PEOPLE	AREA (HECTARES)	Density (Number of persons per hectare)
Ashley	11,168	178	63
Avonmouth	12,177	1,609	8
Bedminster	10,758	254	42
Bishopston	11,996	176	68
Bishopsworth	11,339	356	32
Brislington East	11,511	410	28
Brislington West	10,636	327	33

Figure 5.2 *Research for statistics and information is available online. Here, for example, is some local area data for England and Wales taken from the* Neighbourhood Statistics *website. Students need to develop a high level of research skills to find data, though there are occasions when the teacher may provide a suitable web address for them to use.*

Accuracy of data

It should go without saying that geographical data needs to be accurate to be of any value – for example, for use in making decisions. But obtaining accurate data, or even knowing what 'accurate' means, is not always easy. In the past, when data was not so easily available and could not be cross-checked, the problem of accuracy was not one that could be easily addressed, so its importance tended to be underplayed. This is no longer acceptable. Nowadays it is usually possible to check for accuracy by finding the same data in several different places, both in hard-copy sources and on websites. Sometimes this raises a question as to which of the many sources are the most accurate. Students should be taught to be alert to this problem.

Reliable data

The idea of accuracy is also linked to reliability. It is tempting to regard figures as always being 'facts' that need not be questioned. Figures, however, can be selectively used and presented, sometimes after processing, to make them appear in their best light. So as with any web research, the origin of the numeric data obtained from a web search should always be questioned. This includes finding out the purpose for which the data has been presented.

Quantity of data

Although a large quantity of data is no use without accuracy, it is usually the case that a large amount of data is better than a small sample – for example, when trying to establish patterns or to provide evidence for a decision. Although a large data set can throw up anomalies, at least it is easier to detect anomalies when they are set in a large data sample.

Statistical techniques can be used to test for the data's reliability within pre-determined confidence limits. These techniques depend on the size of the data sample, giving increased reliability as the sample size increases. Both upper and lower limits to the sample sizes can also be identified by statistical techniques. Good-quality geography should include understanding the value of obtaining a suitable amount of data and recognising the tentative nature of conclusions when the sample is low.

Making links

NC Orders for ICT: KS3 PoS Knowledge, skills and understanding

Finding things out

Pupils should be taught:

- how to obtain information well matched to purpose by selecting appropriate sources, using and refining search methods and questioning the plausibility and value of the information found
- how to collect, enter, analyse and evaluate quantitative and qualitative information, checking its accuracy [for example, carrying out a survey of local traffic, analysing data gathered in fieldwork].

Technical standards

There are several ways in which data can be presented. This can be as maps, graphs or tables. Whichever technique is used, the data should be presented to high standards of technical proficiency. The case for doing this when drawing maps is set out in Chapter 4. The same principle should apply to drawing graphs. Although drawing graphs by hand can be an activity that some students enjoy, what is important is that the end result is to the highest possible standard. As with maps, there is usually little comparison between a hand-drawn graph and one that is drawn by a computer. It is hard to make out a case that anything lower than the highest possible standard of technical proficiency should now be accepted as representing good quality-data presentation in geography.

Choice of graphing techniques

The high profile given to data in geography means that a lot of emphasis should be given to developing a knowledge and understanding of the many ways in which it can be presented. At GCSE and even at AS/A2 level, it still seems common for a limited range of techniques to be used. Simple bar graphs, line graphs and charts are commonly used, sometimes when they are appropriate. Often, however, they appear to show either a lack of imagination or a lack of knowledge or ability to produce anything better. Expectations

The area in '000 hectares for Italy's main physical features

	North	Centre	South	Total
Mountains	5530	1578	3503	10611
Hills	2272	3724	6548	12544
Lowland	4187	535	2255	6977
Total	11989	5837	12306	30132

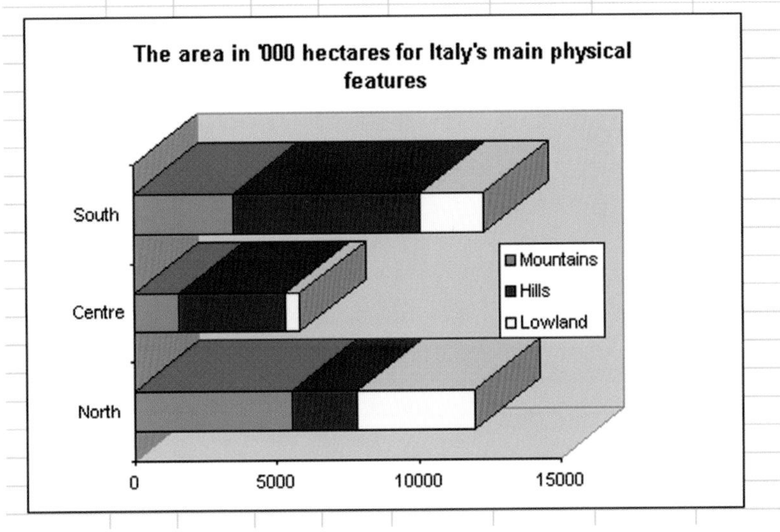

U.S. Census Bureau

Population Pyramid Summary for China

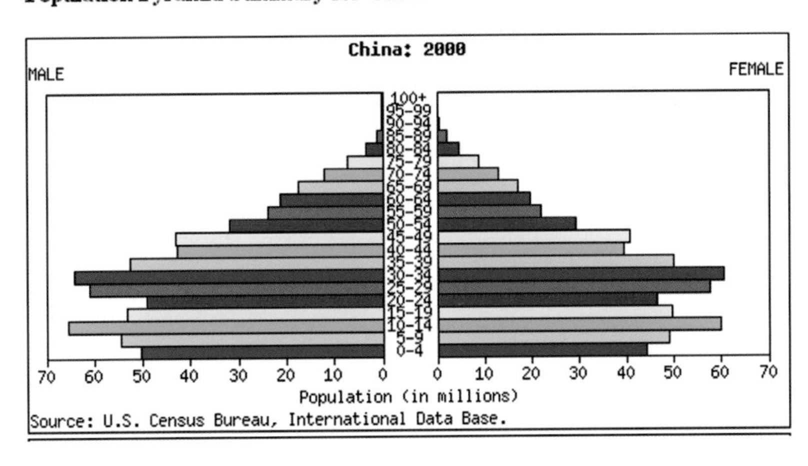

Figure 5.3 *Students can use a wide variety of styles, from a spreadsheet to graph statistical data. It is important for them to develop a knowledge of the types of graph that are available and an understanding of the characteristics of each type so that they choose a type that is appropriate.*

Data: Istat and US Census Bureau

Check it out

Think about the work done by your students in geography to present data in the form of graphs.

- Do you have a phased programme that introduces students to the different types of graphs that are available in a spreadsheet such as Excel?
- Do you explicitly teach your students the characteristics of the different types of graph so that they can make appropriate choices?
- How many different types of graph do you teach?
- Do you provide opportunities for students to make their own choice of graph?

should be higher, especially now that such a wide range of graph styles is available from which to choose. One problem may be the circle of deprivation that begins when students are *not* exposed to a rich variety of graphs for fear that they may have problems in understanding them. This leads to a lack of awareness of their existence, and hence a lack of ability to draw them.

A sign of high-quality work in drawing graphs would be for students to have both the knowledge of what can be produced and the ability to draw them. Whether graphs should be drawn by hand or produced using a computer is another question. Students should also have the ability to understand the characteristics of the graph so that they can interpret it for meaning. That, however, is part of the cognitive domain rather than a matter of knowledge or technical competence.

Data processing

Raw data has to be processed before it can be made meaningful. One way to process it is to apply formulae to it. A formula can be used to find something as simple as a total, a mean or a median. It can also be used for more complex operations, such as to test for relationships between data sets – for example, using a Pearson or Spearman correlation technique. Data can also be processed by using a formula to find a geographical index, such as for population density, economic wealth or a river's hydraulic radius. It may even be that students work out their own index – for example when studying the quality of a local environment by using a litter count or attaching a score to visual impressions.

Whatever the purpose, good-quality work in geography will be characterised by the students' ability to make use of formulae to process raw data, and to use their understanding of the formulae to interpret it. The techniques used should, when relevant, be no less complex than those that the students are expected to use in their maths lessons. If they are more complex, then there are likely to be problems.

Using ICT for data handling

ICT has much to offer geography when working with figures. It combines the characteristics of speed, accuracy and the ability to link data dynamically. It can also provide opportunities for the data to be displayed in a wide range of graphic styles. In this section, examples of ways in which ICT can be used for data handling in geography are presented, though such is the scope of its potential that little other than the basics can be introduced.

Data-handling applications

The main ICT applications designed for handling data are spreadsheets and databases. It is useful to note that, although a database has far greater processing capabilities than are to be found in a spreadsheet, most data-handling work in school geography can probably be done effectively by using a spreadsheet. The facility for inserting a spreadsheet into a word processor creates another useful option – for example, inserting Excel into Word. The effect is to present the data in the form of a table, while retaining the functions of a spreadsheet, swapping easily between the two.

Check it out

Think about the different ways in which work in numeracy plays a role in your department's schemes of work and in public examinations.

- Do you have a coherent plan that links numeracy work in geography to work done in maths?
- Are you aware of the language and techniques that are used to teach students basic work in maths, e.g. in making different types of calculations?
- How does your use of numeracy in geography match with the standards the students should achieve in numeracy in each year?
- Are there any opportunities you can take to make explicit links between work in geography and work in maths, e.g. through fieldwork?

Check it out

There is no shortage of sources for data on the web. Here are some websites that may be useful:

- *Cyberschoolbus: Infonation*
  Graphs and data about countries
- *National Statistics*
- *WorldClimate*
  World climate data
- *Meteorological Office*
  Map of weather stations
- *Transport Statistics*

Technique tip

You can insert a new spreadsheet into a Word document and type the data in.

- Place the cursor where you want to put the spreadsheet.
- Click on the spreadsheet icon or click on Insert, Object and then Microsoft Excel Worksheet.
- Highlight or choose the number of rows and columns you want to appear (you can expand the spreadsheet later).
- When the spreadsheet appears, the spreadsheet toolbar also appears at the top of the document.
- When you finish entering the data, click on the page outside the spreadsheet; the spreadsheet then reverts to looking like a table in the word processor.
- To make the spreadsheet active again, double-click in the table.

Technique tip

To make it easier to read data in a table in Word, you can use the Table AutoFormat tool.

- Click on the table to identify it.
- Click on Table, then AutoFormat.
- Choose one of the formats, e.g. List 1 or 3D effects 2.

Technique tip

You can create a table of data in a word processor, then transfer it to a spreadsheet.

- Select the table in the word processor.
- Click on Edit, then Copy.
- Open a spreadsheet (e.g. in Excel).
- Paste the table into cell A1 in the spreadsheet; the data is then put automatically into the right number of cells in the spreadsheet. Unlike with copying and pasting in a spreadsheet, you do not need to select the exact number of cells to match the data.

It is useful to remember that GIS programs also contain data-handling functions, allowing the data to be linked to points, areas or lines on a map. This involves entering data in a database and setting up fields in records, each record being identified by a map code that is located on the map. This aspect of data handling is considered in more detail in Chapter 4.

File Edit View Insert Format Tools Data Window Help

Arial 10

F22 =

	A	B	C	D	E	F	G
1		Income per head in dollars	Life expectancy at birth	Energy consumption	Daily food supply (calories)	Illiteracy rate	Population per nurse
2							
3	**Mozambique**	80	47	85	1680	67	5480
4	**Somalia**	120	48	64	1906	76	1900
5	**Nepal**	170	52	25	2077	74	4680
6	**Bangladesh**	210	52	57	2021	65	8530
7	**Rwanda**	310	48	41	1971	50	3690
8	**China**	370	70	598	2639	27	1610
9	**Morocco**	950	62	247	3020	51	1050
10	**Paraguay**	1110	67	232	2757	10	1000
11	**Jamaica**	1500	73	931	2609	5	490
12	**Mexico**	2490	70	1300	3052	13	880
13	**Yugoslavia**	3060	72	2409	3634	7	250
14	**Saudi Arabia**	7050	64	5033	2874	38	340
15	**Spain**	11020	76	2201	3572	5	260
16	**New Zealand**	12680	75	4971	3362	5	80
17	**United Kingdom**	16100	76	3646	3149	5	
18	**U Arab Emirates**	19860	72	10874	3309	5	390
19	**USA**	21790	76	7822	3671	5	70
20	**Japan**	25430	79	3563	2956	5	180

Weather station **SHEFFIELD** is at about 53.40°N 1.50°W.

Average Temperature

	Jan	Feb	Mar	Apr	May	Jun	Jul	Aug	Sep	Oct	Nov	Dec	Year
°C	3.8	3.9	5.4	7.8	10.9	14.1	15.9	15.6	13.4	9.9	6.5	4.4	9.3
°F	38.8	39.0	41.7	46.0	51.6	57.4	60.6	60.1	56.1	49.8	43.7	39.9	48.7

Figure 5.4 *Data can be presented as raw data in a spreadsheet table.*

Data: World Climate

Tables of data

The easiest way to record and present raw data is to enter it into a table. This can be done in a word processor such as Word, or a spreadsheet such as Excel. Looking at the raw data in a table can be effective, but only when the data set is not too big. The advantage of using a table is that one still has the raw figures to look at and compare. The problem is that there may be no visual clues to help you make sense of the data – in contrast to a graph, for example, where size, shape and colour can help to identify a pattern or trend. It is, of course, possible to use colour in a table. The figures, text or cells can be coloured to separate the data and make it easier to see.

One option is to use the automatic functions of a spreadsheet to colour the data against given parameters. This can be done by using the Conditional

Formatting tool from the Format menu in Excel. This tool gives the option of choosing either exact figures or ranges of figures, which may be coloured and also shown in a different font style. For example, all figures above or between certain given figures can be automatically shown in a different colour. This is a useful way of helping children with mapping when they have to put raw data into colour ranges. The colour for each category of data can be matched to the colour in the table, making it easier to match the data more accurately to the right category.

Get it sorted

There are times when the use of ICT may not be appropriate, such as when the task could be done more quickly without a computer. It would, for example, be quick and easy to sort a list of five towns by hand into the order of their population, or a short list of rivers into the order of their length. This task, however, is far from quick and easy if the list is longer, or if there are several variables to sort. This is where ICT can play a part. Immediately following the command to sort the data, the operation is performed both instantly and with total accuracy, irrespective of the amount of data.
In geography, this facility for sorting data can be used to create lists in order of importance or to see how data sets in different data fields compare with each other – for example, to show relationships between data. The rank order of one set of data can be visually compared to the rank order for data that may be related to it. Further processing of the data will be needed for a more accurate result.

Technique tip

Here is the technique for sorting data in an Excel spreadsheet:

- Select the data you want to sort.
- Click on the Data menu, then the Sort tool.
- Choose the column by which you want to sort the data.
- Choose the order, whether ascending or descending.
- Make sure you select the whole data set when you do this so that all the columns are sorted at the same time.

Classifying data

Data collection for an enquiry needs to be planned in advance. This is likely to involve creating categories so that the data can be entered quickly, then processing and presenting it when the research has been completed. The rows and columns in a spreadsheet or a table provide a visual structure in which to enter data. Headings have to be created, whether at the top of columns in a spreadsheet or table, or as fields in a database. Once the structure has been set up, the data can be collected and entered in a way

Teaching idea

The students can use the Sort tool in a spreadsheet or table to help them make decisions about the categories to use when drawing a map. The Sort tool will put the data into order so that it is easier to identify where the boundaries between categories should be made.

A sorted data table can be copied and pasted into a basic drawing program such as Paint. This can be done after a base map has been opened and moved to the centre of the screen. Students can then have the sorted data and a base map on the same screen. This makes it easier to produce a shaded map of the data.

that is neat and ordered. Classification is one of the first steps towards making sense of raw data, so this initial part of the planning can be invaluable. An alternative is to collect the raw data, then to process it to see if any kinds of categories are created naturally. Figures may cluster, for example, or may form a pattern that creates a meaningful structure. The facility in ICT for copying or cutting and pasting raw data makes it easy to rearrange it as required.

Seek and find

It can be cumbersome to work with a large amount of data, especially if a particular numerical value has to be found. This may be a single number or word in a spreadsheet or database. As with other ICT applications, there is a tool to search for anything, whether text or number.

Technique tip

Use the Seek tool (Find tool in Excel) in the Edit menu to find a specific item of data in a spreadsheet.

Although data can be searched in a spreadsheet, the ability to set up a more complex query is only available when data is entered in a database. This allows for a query to find anything from a field in the records that is above, below, equal to or between different numerical values. It could be used, for example, to identify only those countries that have a GNP per head that is above a given figure, or countries where the daily calorie intake is below a given figure. The data can then be further investigated to see if there are spatial patterns that will help to explain it.

Teaching idea

Give students data about a range of countries or about regions within a country. (An alternative might be to get them to research their own data.) Using the data, ask them to:

- work out a mean figure for each column (field) of data
- work out a correlation figure for different pairs of data.

The data can then be analysed for meaning, e.g. the extent to which the data sets might have a causal relationship.

Teaching idea

Provide the students with raw data in a spreadsheet that relates to the location of an economic activity – for example, the location of a distribution depot. They can use the data to work out the economic cost of different locations.

Then change one of the key variables – for example, building a new road that shortens distance or reduces time so that the transport costs are reduced.

The students can then recalculate the costs, using the program's automatic functions to work out the figures.

Using formulae

Formulae can be used in data handling for making any kind of calculation with the data. This could include finding a total, a mean or a more complex statistical index such as for correlation. The tools for doing this in a spreadsheet or database do not require any knowledge of how the formula is worked out. All it needs is to click the correct icon or to follow the wizard that sets it up.

Separate calculations do not have to be made for every item. Once the formula has been created for one cell, it can be dragged to apply to the cells beside or below it. This is useful, for example, when working out the population density of a set of countries. The formula only needs to be created for one set of cells so that an answer is worked out. The formula for the calculation can then be dragged down to apply to all the other cells.

Some programs have been specially written for work in geography – for example, to help process and present field study data. These contain the relevant formulae such as the various indices that are used to measure stream discharge or pebble roundness. It is important for students to be taught how to work out these formulae for themselves. However, it is questionable as to whether they should be expected to spend so much time working them out by hand on every subsequent occasion. Time working out a correlation formula, for example, can be better spent in analysing its meaning.

Modelling with data

According to the NC Orders for ICT, students need to handle data in order to test out ideas and make predictions. This is the same as asking 'what if?' questions in geography. An example might be to ask what it would cost to relocate an industry in a site where costs were different, or how the scenic value of a landscape could be changed if something new was built. It is easy to change data in one or more variables in a spreadsheet, then let the program's automatic functions recalculate the results. Even the appearance of graphs will change because of the dynamic link between data and graph.

Making links

NC Orders for ICT: KS3 PoS Developing ideas and making things happen

Pupils should be taught:

- how to use ICT to test predictions and discover patterns and relationships, by exploring, evaluating and developing models and changing their rules and values.

Drawing graphs

As with drawing maps, the technical quality of graphs drawn by ICT can not be bettered. This quality should set the standard against which all graphs should be assessed, at least with respect to this particular criterion. It is not a valid argument to say that the standard expected should be kept lower because not all students have access to ICT. It is simply the case that times have moved on and both standards and expectations need to move on with them.

Nor is it acceptable to say that the student's choice of graph should be limited because of the problems involved in drawing a particular style such as an effective 3-D graph or a pie graph with an 'exploded' section. Provided the choice is appropriate, the students should be expected to choose the style of graph that is most appropriate, not only to the features of the data, but also to what they want the data to show most clearly.

The tools for creating graphs in a spreadsheet are generally easy to use, though the default style is not always the most appropriate for some types of geographical data. There can also be some problems with the default choice of the data that is presented on each axis. There are, however, options for changing the default choice. It is also relatively easy to change the default colours and other graph basics so that the most visually effective graph is produced.

Graphs drawn in a spreadsheet or database can be copied and pasted into a word-processed document. Scissors and glue should be things of the past. The seamless features of ICT should facilitate an end result that at least looks professional. Although neatness should not generally be a criterion for assessment in geography, it should certainly be taken into account in relation to illustrations such as graphs and maps.

Teaching idea

Provide the students with a data set that shows the climate as temperature and rainfall for a selection of UK holiday resorts. Allocate a different resort to pairs or groups. The challenge is for each pair or group to choose and produce the style of graph that is visually most effective in showing why their resort has the best climate for a holiday.

Teaching idea

Students can access population data for the USA and other countries from the US Census website. This site also has a function that draws population pyramids for every country. Type 'population pyramid' in the site's Search tool.

Website
US Census Bureau

Teaching idea

One of the teaching resources on the BECTA website is for students to select rogue data from data on development in different countries. This technique can be adapted for use with other topics.

Website
BECTA: Exemplifying ICT Use in Geography: Data, data everywhere

Teaching idea

One of the teaching resources on the BECTA website is for students to draw population graphs. Use or adapt this activity.

Website
BECTA: Exemplifying ICT Use in Geography: Analysing population data

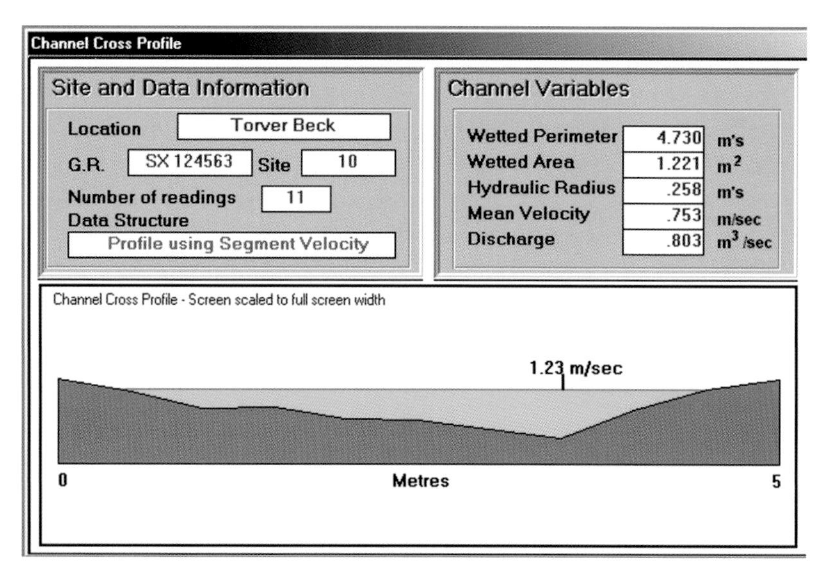

Figure 5.5 *A fieldwork data-handling program can be used to record, present and process data. This example is the Channel program from Geopacks. This specialist program can draw multiple river channel profiles and show statistical calculations such as hydraulic radius.*

Wider issues in data handling with ICT

Data handling in geography needs to be set in the wider context of when and how students will handle data in other subjects. This is part of the rationale that lies behind the Secondary (KS3) Strategy for Mathematics. It also needs to be set within the context of requirements for ICT work as listed in the NC Orders for ICT, the KS3 Strategy for ICT and the ICTAC guidance documents. These documents relate both to how data handling is taught and to the principles that lie behind data processing and presentation. Geography teachers need to be aware of these contexts and make use of them to their advantage.

Skills transfer

ICT is good with figures. Many students of geography are not. Even some geography teachers find that working with figures is challenging. It is, however, often disturbing to note how the students' ability in a maths classroom often seems to exceed their ability to apply it to their work in geography. Perhaps the link with ICT software through data-handling programs such as Excel and Access may help to break down this psychological barrier and enable them to transfer their skills more easily across subject boundaries. A more coherent approach to teaching data handling across subjects, such as that advocated by the ICTAC documents, should also be helpful.

Make it make sense

Although ICT is good with figures, it is always useful to remember the well-known adage 'garbage in, garbage out'. The professional appearance of data

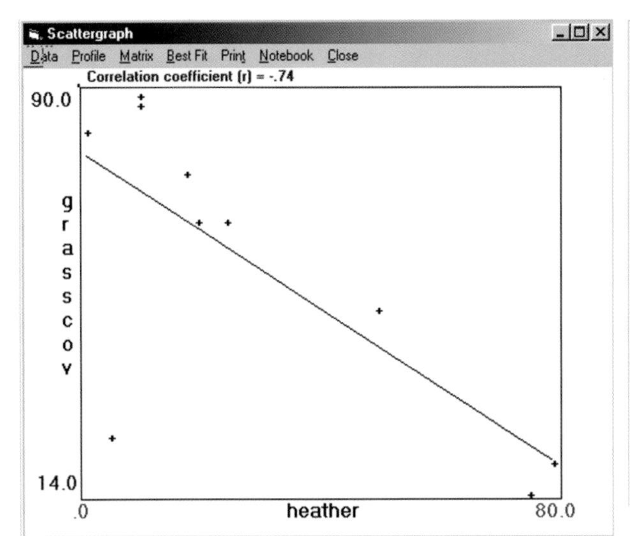

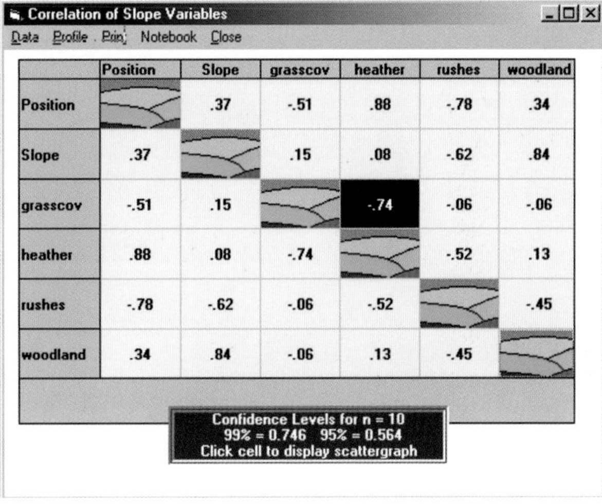
Correlation of Slope Variables

Data Profile Print Notebook Close

	Position	Slope	grasscov	heather	rushes	woodland
Position		.37	-.51	.88	-.78	.34
Slope	.37		.15	.08	-.62	.84
grasscov	-.51	.15		-.74	-.06	-.06
heather	.88	.08	-.74		-.52	.13
rushes	-.78	-.62	-.06	-.52		-.45
woodland	.34	.84	-.06	.13	-.45	

Confidence Levels for n = 10
99% = 0.746 95% = 0.564
Click cell to display scattergraph

Figure 5.6 *Specialist field study software from the Geopacks suite of programs can carry out powerful statistical calculations from field study data that students collect.*

© Geopacks 08705 133168

presented through the use of ICT has to be set against its unquestioning ability to produce whatever is requested of it, even when entirely inappropriate and guided by the default style. It is only when the data is incorrectly entered that the program will fail to produce a result.

Making the choice

The choice of formulae and styles of graph, made available through the use of ICT, has to be a new focus for teaching. Geography teachers need to look carefully at the styles that are possible and relevant for work in geography, such as the style that is suitable for drawing a climate graph. They then need to give students guidance in finding and using them. Any time saved by the use of ICT will need to be used to ensure that students understand how to make appropriate choices, for example, of types of graph and of formulae. Doing this should help to raise standards in visual literacy as well as in data handling. Although there is an element of personal preference in what seems effective in the visual appearance of a graph, students need to be made aware that a graph needs to be appropriate for an audience. They should also consider that their own preferences may be rather different. As with maps, garish colours on a graph may appeal to some but not to others. The age and understanding of the audience also should be considered when these choices are being made.

Achieving progression

There is a valid argument to be made that students also need to be able to handle data in the traditional way, i.e. by working out formulae and drawing graphs by hand. There is, however, likely to come a time when there is no scope for further progression, so that little further is served by ensuring that students continue to work in this way. There are, for example, limits to progression in drawing a bar graph or a pie diagram or in the ability to work

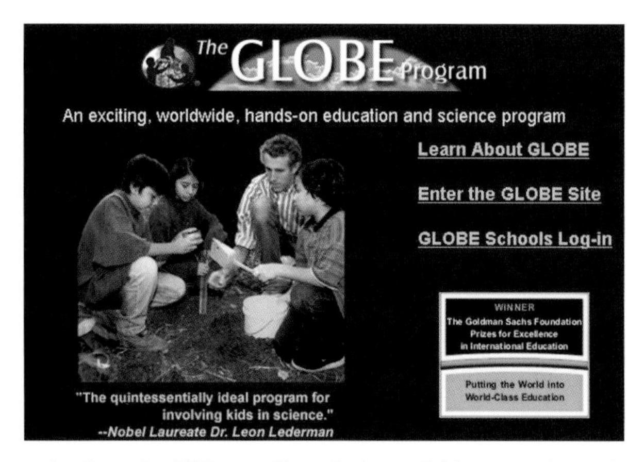

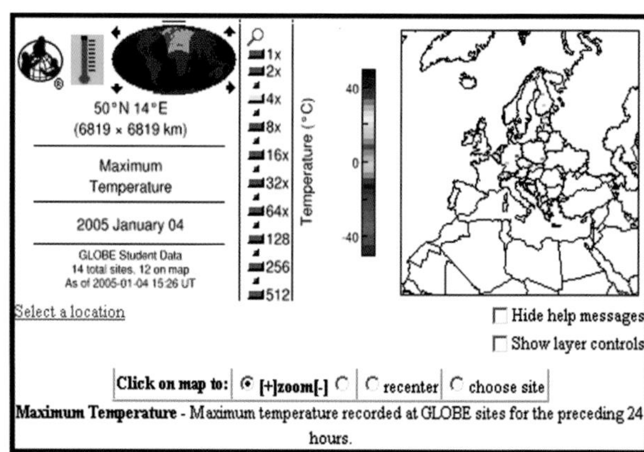

Figure 5.7 *The GLOBE Program is an international project that involves students in collecting environmental data and sharing it with others on a website.*

The source of this material is the GLOBE website at www.globe.gov

out a formula. ICT can offer a faster, reliably accurate and technically more proficient way of handling data – indeed, in a way that ought to set the standard. It is justifiable to introduce students progressively to a wider range of graphs and formulae, as well as making sure that they understand their characteristics. However, it cannot be justifiable to expect them to continue to demonstrate the same level of competence in a limited range of graph styles and formulae over several years. Some guidance as to what can be expected of students' data-handling capabilities in different years can be identified from the Secondary (KS3) Strategy for Mathematics. This can help to inform geography teachers of what they could be doing, both to save time in geography lessons and to extend the students' understanding of data handling.

Perfect results every time

Graphic skills, including the processing of data, form part of the assessment criteria for work in geography at every level. As with maps, this raises the question of the criteria against which graphs and calculations should be assessed. Graphs drawn with ICT will be technically perfect every time. The calculations will also be correct, provided the data has been input correctly and the formula has been typed correctly. The result of using ICT is that every student can produce identical high-quality results. This is something to celebrate and it will certainly be appreciated by the students themselves. But there is a problem: some might feel that there is little point in giving a mark for something for which there can be no gradation of marks. There are, of course, other aspects of the marking criteria for drawing graphs, such as the ability to make an appropriate choice and to analyse the data. But perhaps the time has come when no purpose is served by giving a mark for what the computer has done!

Chapter 6 The ICT in pictures

Key questions

- How can photos help teaching and learning to be effective in geography?
- What is the link between visual literacy and photo interpretation in geography?
- What ICT applications are needed to work with photos?
- What techniques and tools in different ICT applications can be used to present and process images?
- How can students use ICT to work with photos so as to enhance their geographical knowledge and understanding?

ICT applications

- Sources of images:
  web browsers
  CD-Rom.
- Image processing:
  Paint Shop Pro
  Paint
  Corel Draw
  Imaging for Windows
- Working with images:
  Word
  PowerPoint
  PhotoJam
  Geopacks Slide Show Manager.

Focus on photos

In geography, photos are more than just a means of illustration, though even this limited function is of some value. It is certainly hard to match the power of a good-quality photograph shown on a big screen to illustrate what a place looks like. Photos can also help visual learners to access knowledge and ideas in geography, i.e. they help with the 'V' in 'VAK'.

In addition to their powers of illustration, photos can:

- provide a key resource that helps students to understand places, patterns and processes
- bring colour, detail and mood to a landscape in a way that cannot be done by text alone
- help convey a sense of scale, though they are still confined to a computer monitor or wall screen
- engage students in developing an insight into the values and viewpoints that people hold about places – for example, by considering photo content, composition and selection
- complement a sketch – perhaps at times even replace it – as a means of recording data in the field.

Work in geography can involve different types of photos:

- Ground views can show everything from a panoramic landscape to close-up detail.
- Oblique air photos can add a perspective and a better sense of location to landscape features.
- Vertical air photos give details about an area that maps do not show, while photos taken from space provide a global perspective that can give a very different sense of proportion.

Making links

NC Geography Orders: KS3 PoS

Enquiry skills enable pupils to:
- ask relevant questions
- pose and define problems.

Reasoning skills enable pupils to:
- draw inferences and make deductions
- make judgements and decisions informed by reasons or evidence.

Creative thinking skills enable pupils to:
- be imaginative in their thinking.

Evaluation skills enable pupils to:
- evaluate information they are given
- judge the value of what they read, hear and do [include 'see'].

- Photos at different scales from different heights can play a part in helping students to understand the lens through which geographers study places.
- Images captured by remote sensing, although not photographs, can be processed to give a high level of photo-realism.
- Photos can be either still or movie images – both of them easily captured in digital form.

ICT can play a part in bringing photos to students as part of the seamless interface that exists between the different digital formats and technologies. Photos can be integrated with text, annotated and edited, all within almost any ICT application. This can be in a word processor, a drawing program, a spreadsheet or GIS software. They can also be shown on an interactive whiteboard via the IW software.

Geographical quality in working with photos

The NC Orders for Geography mention photos in a list of secondary sources that students should be able to select and use. There is also mention of using a camera as an element of field study techniques, though this is illustrative rather than statutory. Yet behind these fleeting references is a plethora of skills and ideas that need to be taught so that photos can be used effectively in geographical study. At higher levels, photos are no less important as sources of evidence – usually in association with maps, diagrams and text. They are, for example, part of decision-making exercises at GCSE and AS/A2 levels. At GCSE level, exam board feedback often includes comments to the effect that students are less skilled in photo interpretation than in map reading. Perhaps they are less willing to state the obvious that they can see, or perhaps they find it more difficult to extract meaning from data that is so visually comprehensive and often taken from an unusual angle. There can be more to a photo than meets the eye!

High-quality work with photos in geography is likely to relate to the following:

- photo selection
- image size and quality
- use of colour
- interpretation skills.

The extent to which ICT can play a part in helping to develop high-quality work is very much determined by these factors.

Selecting photos

Selecting photos carries the implication that there is a choice from which to select. This can be difficult when only a few photos are available in a textbook. More photos could be found by wider research in magazines and other reference books. This, however, is seldom an easy process, made more difficult by the problems of bringing them together in one place and in one format.

Check it out

Think about the extent to which your classroom, or any other room in which geography is taught, is suitable for showing students a good range of high-quality digital photos on a big screen.

- Is the screen in a fixed position for constant use?
- Is the screen large enough to be seen clearly by all students?
- Do you have an interactive whiteboard on which to use photo activities?
- Do projected images reflect back from a shiny surface, or does the screen have a matt surface?
- Does the classroom have adequate blackout?
- Is there a permanently fixed data projector linked to a computer in the classroom?
- Is the data projector secured to prevent theft?
- Is there access to a bank of high-quality photos?

If the answer to any of these questions is 'no', you will not be able to make the most effective use of digital technology to show photos.

- Work out what it would need, and how much it would cost, to create the optimum conditions.
- Find out if there are any sources of finance in the school, nationally or from elsewhere that would help to create the optimum conditions.

Making links

NC Orders for ICT: KS3 PoS

In developing geographical skills, pupils should be taught:

- to select and use appropriate fieldwork techniques [e.g. land-use survey, data logging] and instruments [e.g. cameras]
- to select and use secondary sources of evidence, including photographs (including vertical and oblique aerial photographs), satellite images and evidence from ICT-based sources [e.g. from the internet].

The ability to select photos can indicate not only an appreciation of the power of an image to convey information, but also an understanding of different people's perceptions of places. A choice of images, for example, could show a place to be one that is either attractive to visit or one to avoid. Selecting photos can also demonstrate an ability to show what is either unique or typical about a place. So for work with photos to be effective, a whole bank of photos is essential. This is a case where more is likely to be better.

Teaching idea

Assemble a set of about 10 photos of a place. Ask the students to present a particular image or impression of the place by each selecting only two photos from the set. Give different groups a different perspective, and see what they choose to show. A good example might be set of photos of a tourist resort, and you could ask them to select photos which might:

- attract parents with young children
- attract elderly people
- attract new business to the area, creating jobs
- show environmental concern.

The students can then present and explain their choices.

Photo size and quality

For work in geography, high-quality photos are likely to be of greater use than those whose reproduction is poor. The best quality will come from direct photo prints, though these are costly to produce and prohibitively expensive to reproduce in bulk. The photos in books or other printed sources will normally be printed as a series of fine dots, rather than appearing as photographic prints. Cheap production on poor-quality paper gives the kind of grainy reproduction that is acceptable in a newspaper but rare in today's geography textbooks. Poor-quality photos can also be found on websites. This is usually deliberate as a means of saving download time, the problem being that good-quality digital photos are disk-hungry. But for detail and realism, the general principle must be that large, good-quality photos will be of most use in geography.

Colour photos

There is little use for monochrome (black-and-white) photographs for work in geography, other than for comparing images with the past when colour photos were not available. Perhaps an exception to this is the specialist use of some monochrome vertical air photos, though colour vertical air photos are still likely to be better for use in schools. Colour will help a student to interpret a photo – for example, by identifying signs of drought in crops, or different types of plant species. School textbooks have been entirely in colour for at least the last 20 years as the cost of printing has come down, largely due to the fact that many books are now printed in countries with lower labour and other costs. It can make an interesting activity for work in geography to find out where the textbook has been printed.

Teaching idea

Carry out map and photo research on websites to see how a place has changed over the last 100 years. Here are some examples:

- a town centre to show how shops and traffic have changed
- landforms that have changed, e.g. a glacier that has advanced or retreated
- historic photos of a volcano, e.g. before and after a major eruption
- how a tourist honeypot site has changed, e.g. from a fishing village to a seaside resort.

Check it out

Compare the different ways of showing big colour photos to students.

- How do you think that the quality of photos compares between using a slide projector with 35-mm transparencies, a data projector, an overhead projector and poster-size photos?
- Which do you find easier to use: a slide projector or a computer?
- Are digital image files easier to store and retrieve than 35-mm slides?

Photo interpretation

As with maps, the main thinking part of working with photos comes with photo interpretation. At the most basic level, the student needs a 'geographical eye' to see what is there, accompanied by the geographical vocabulary to describe it. Interpretation involves analysis and the ability to suggest reasons for what is in the scene. This involves using the limited evidence that the photo contains and perhaps in addition using evidence from other sources. Interpretation also involves the investigative and critical skills for evaluating information about who took the photo, when it was taken and, often crucially, why it was taken. All of this information is seldom available in books, though a list of photo credits is always given from which some information can be gleaned. For further information, additional research is usually needed. Without this information, the reliability of the photo as a source of evidence needs to be questioned and, at the very least, cross-checked against other photos.

Teaching idea

Present the students with a photo and set up a template for interpreting it. You could provide additional help by locating it on a map with a postcode or grid reference.

- Who took it?
- When did they take it?
- Why might they have taken it?
- What is there that one can describe?
- What explanations could one give for what is happening in it?

Check it out

When in your schemes of work do you provide opportunities for students to develop photo interpretation skills?

Does work in geography require any photo interpretation skills in common with any other subject, e.g. history? If so, do you share a common approach to developing this aspect of visual literacy?

Using ICT for photos

The seamless nature of ICT means that, provided the software can support the different image formats, photos can be used with any kind of ICT application. They can be captured and copied from websites or inserted from a file into a word processor, presentation software, a spreadsheet, a multi-media authoring program or a web authoring program. Some GIS software also allows you to insert photos and link them dynamically to a map so that, if you click on a map hotspot, the photo will appear.

Check it out

Think about the importance you give to using photos with your students.

- When did you last show students a big photo on a wall screen?
- How often do you show your students photos projected on a wall screen?
- Do you think you should use this strategy more than you do at present?

Choice of photos

The choice of good photos available in digital form is almost limitless. They are available on CD-Roms or websites, or can be taken with a digital camera. Photo prints or photos in books can be scanned and thereby changed to a digital format. Even 35-mm transparencies can be converted to a digital format, as can analogue video material. There is indeed no image that cannot be converted to a digital format. The present generation of mobile phones have built-in digital cameras that allow photos to be taken, then sent to another mobile phone or as an e-mail attachment. This mobile technology has considerable potential for work in geography. Any photo can be copied or captured from source, using one technique or another. There is also a good chance that photos from websites will be accompanied by some information about their origin.

Figure 6.1 *A digital camera can be used to capture the moment in a way that a field sketch cannot. This image shows a goat eating leaves from a tree on the Greek island of Rhodes. Digital photos can also capture the colour and weather of a scene on a particular day.*

Quality, format and copyright

There can sometimes be an issue over the quality of photos. Photos captured from websites may be of relatively poor quality. This may be because they have been either taken in low resolution or, as is more likely, saved in a way that makes them open more quickly on-screen. Selections of photos are sometimes presented as thumbnails, especially when they are on the website for commercial sale, and where using them can involve questions of copyright. As with other web sources, but especially with photos, students need to be made aware of the copyright laws, though there is probably little chance of them contravening these laws. Teachers, however, may need to exercise rather more caution when printing multiple copies of images on which there is copyright. They also need to take care when putting photos on

Teaching idea

This idea is based on the 'odd one out' principle:

- Assemble a series of photos with three photos in each set. The three photos should have something in common. You could do this by inserting photos into PowerPoint slides.
- Then choose one of the photos from each set and move it to one of the other sets. Do this by cutting and pasting one of each of the photo sets.
- Show the students the sets of three photos. The students choose one of the three photos that they think is the odd one out.
- When they have finished, they could try to reassemble the odd ones to make the sets you began with, by finding something in common between the three.
- You may have a 'right' answer in mind, but you should be prepared for students to reassemble the photos in a different way. Discuss the reasons for their choices.

Websites

Corbis
Lycos: Tripod Image Gallery
The Geo-Images Project (USA)
Geography Photos
Subscription site
FreeFoto
Photo gallery
Free Images
Unesco Photobank
British Geomorphological Research Group: Educational Resources
Urban75

a departmental website that has open access. There is, however, enough freely available material to avoid these problems, and if there is still a problem, buying a digital camera can provide the answer.

For most work in geography, the highest quality of photos is not usually needed, though there are limits. A poor-quality image shown on a big screen can be ineffective, while an image that is enlarged too far can break down into visible pixels. Photos taken with a digital camera can still be perfectly acceptable, even at relatively low resolution, and saved in JPG format at no more than about 60 kb of disk space. Higher-quality images can take much longer to load, especially on an older computer with a modest speed.

Slide shows

It is easy to create a simple slide show in presentation software such as PowerPoint. Each slide serves as a separate image that can run in a sequence. The presentation can be either set to run by clicking when ready,

Check it out

Think about these aspects of using digital images:

- When and in what context do students learn about the file formats that are used for photos? Is this done in ICT lessons, in art or in another subject?
- Do you understand the laws about copyright and how they apply to using photos from websites?

Websites

BECTA: Introduction to copyright issues for websites

Making links

NC Orders for ICT: KS3 PoS

Exchanging and sharing information

Pupils should be taught:

- to use a range of ICT tools efficiently to draft, bring together and refine information and create good-quality presentations in a form that is sensitive to the needs of particular audiences and suits the information content.

or on a timer to run automatically. Sometimes, an automatic sequence set to music rather than to words can create a special effect, whereby the students' own imaginations and feelings can take over from a teacher's erudite and technical commentary.

PowerPoint defaults to presenting slides in a set order. This style of presentation is suited to a passive audience who simply want to sit and listen to a lecture. It is not, therefore, entirely suitable for working with a class of students with whom constant interaction is needed. Fortunately, it is easy enough to build in an option for hyperlinking to other slides, even in a different file, during a presentation. This allows the teacher to respond to questions as they arise. An alternative is to use a more flexible kind of program that allows for the pictures to be shown in any order. A multi-media authoring program such as Opus can do this by using buttons to link to any slide in any order. The same can be done using web authoring software, or by putting the photos into interactive whiteboard software.

Even if nothing else is available, or if a teacher's ICT skills are limited, a presentation can be created using nothing more than a word processor. Do this by inserting photos into a file and then adjust them for size. Show them by scrolling down the file.

Technique tip

Photos can be saved as files in several types of file format. Some file formats are not compatible with some types of software, though it is unlikely that this will be a problem with any of the formats listed below. The BMP (bitmap) format gives a good-quality image, but it takes a large amount of disk space.

- The JPG format is suitable for most photos and other images that are used for school resources and put on a website. A JPG file takes up about a tenth of the file space occupied by an image taken at the same resolution that has been saved as a BMP.
- The PSP format is unique to the Paint Shop Pro drawing program. It does not open in Word or other general Office programs. When saving an image you have captured in Paint Shop Pro, make sure you check the format before you save.
- The GIF format is another type of compressed file format that is commonly used on websites.

Technique tip

One way to design a page with text and photos is to use a desktop publishing program such as Publisher. This lets you move both text and images around the page by clicking and dragging on the text and image boxes.

You can also use Word to design a page with text and photos:

- From the Insert menu, choose Picture.
- Choose From File.
- Click on Insert to insert the file.

When the photo appears, it may have a black box with eight small black squares (handles) on it. In this format, the photo can only be moved by clicking on the alignment icons, i.e. those for left, centre or right justification.

To give complete flexibility, you need to change the format to one that lets the image 'float' over the page. An image that can do this has white handles.

- Click on the image.
- Click on Format, then Picture (or right-click on the image and choose Format Picture).
- Click on Layout.
- Click on In front of text, then OK.

You can now drag the image to any part of the screen. It is now completely independent of the text, so you may need to adjust the text line length by using the ruler or another method.

Teaching idea

Provide the students with a set of photos that would form a route – for example, from the centre of a town to its outer edge, or a transect through a sand dune system. Get the students to arrange the photos into an appropriate order. They could do this along a map or diagram of the route.

An option might be to present this activity as a visitors' trail. Notes could be added to the photos to show features of interest.

Teaching idea

The *Global Eye* website has a set of slides with activities based on the cocaine trade. Students could use these photos to complete the activities. A similar photo trail could be devised for other topics, e.g. how trainers, microchips and foods come to the UK.

Website

Global Eye: The Cocaine Chain
An example of a photo trail

Annotations and labels

One thing you cannot do with 35-mm transparencies is annotate them, unless they are screened on a whiteboard. Nor is it possible to add animation effects. ICT tools let you do both. Using these techniques can be useful when you

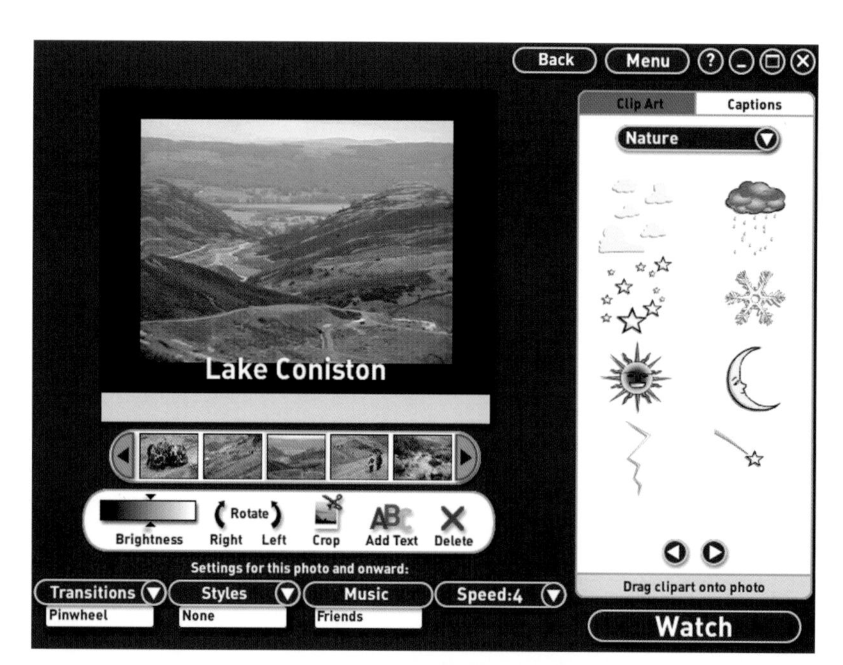

Figure 6.2 *The PhotoJam program contains options for producing a visually interesting slide show with transitions, labels and sound that can help to capture attention and stimulate thought.*

Teaching idea

Get the students to combine a slide show of photos with some music or sounds. The aim is to use the music to help convey the mood of the photos. Another approach could be to convey a message through the words of a song.

Check it out

Think about how you use digital images with students of different ages:

- What do you think might be the maximum number of photos to present to students in different year groups in order to make them memorable and effective?
- There is often a temptation to use too many, but what is too many and how does this differ between students?

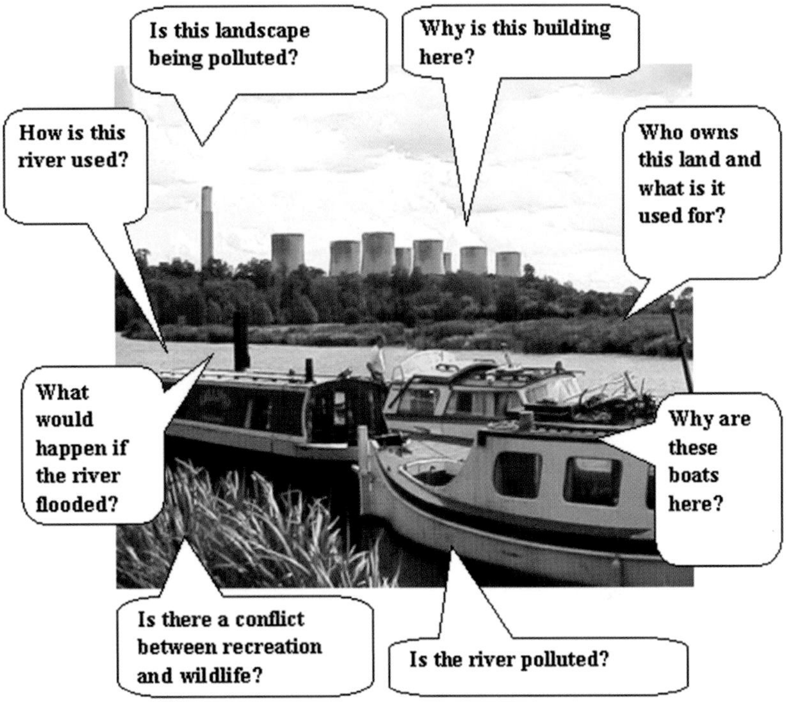

Figure 6.3 *Photos can be shown in PowerPoint with questions made to appear in callouts, either pre-prepared or written in response to questions that the students suggest. This could also be done on an interactive whiteboard by students writing their questions then changing them into type, using SMARTboard software, for example.*

Technique tip

There are several ways to create a slide show in PowerPoint. Here is one method:

- Open a new file in PowerPoint.
- Choose the Blank template option.
- Choose a layout with a text box for a title page.
- For all other slides, choose the blank page layout for the photos.
- Insert a photo on each slide using the Insert tool.
- Adjust the size of the photo to fill the slide.

You can create a more lively presentation by adding callouts from AutoShapes, and adding labels and questions that point to key features.

want to discuss the content of photos with a class. Questions or labels can be made to appear over the photos, either creating discussion points or identifying features using correct geographical vocabulary. This allows the teacher to engage in a dialogue during which the students also have a constant visual backup to what is being discussed. One way to do this is to create the presentation in PowerPoint, using the callout boxes in which to write questions or labels. The same effect can be achieved by using the tools in interactive whiteboard software such as SMART Notebook. Labels can be added, moved to new positions or painted over until revealed by the rubber. In these ways, the teacher can interact with the students, instead of regarding them as a passive audience as each bullet point appears.

The students themselves can annotate or add notes to a photo that is shown on an interactive whiteboard. Text can be dragged around and located beside different features. A final touch might be to convert a student's handwritten text to print, using a tool in the interactive whiteboard software. Although this is effective when the word is correctly transformed, it can produce unfortunate results when it is not!

Animated arrows or other types of drawing can be added to photos to draw attention to how a part of the photo could change, or some other process that involves movement. Arrows, for example, could show the direction of a river's flow or how far a glacier has retreated or advanced.

Teaching idea

Show a photo on an interactive whiteboard. The students can work in groups for a few minutes to think of some questions they want to ask about the photo. One student from each group then comes to the front to write their questions.

Photos to make you think

A single well-chosen photo shown through any kind of program can help to make an effective start to a lesson. The photo could be one that is awe-inspiring, humorous or from an unusual angle, or that goes against a stereotype or is perhaps a little quirky. It can be used to capture interest as a starter activity, or as a focus for work during a plenary. There are many ways to use it – for example, to get the students to raise questions, to guess where it is, to write a caption or comments, or other simple techniques to get them to think. As a memory test, the teacher can use the mute control on the data projector, then ask some questions about it. The students might prefer to call this a quiz.

Two photos on the same screen can be used as a 'compare and contrast' activity. You could, for example, present photos of two river valleys, and get the students to identify the features that are common to both, then to identify ways in which they are different. This is a useful way to bring out the key features of a landform or human feature, as well as identifying the uniqueness of each place. Three photos can be used for an 'odd one out' activity, or to see if the students can find a connection between all three.

Although these activities do not need a computer and data projector, especially if only one photo is used, they are much easier to create and present if you have one. The activity can then be saved and used by another teacher. Although digital files can become corrupted, this is nothing compared to the relatively short lifespan of printed photos if they are handled by the students.

Technique tip

You can add labels around a photo in Word or in PowerPoint. One way to do this is to write in text boxes that you can move into position. A more interesting way is to use a Callout from the AutoShapes menu.

- First, make sure the Drawing toolbar is visible. Do this from the Toolbars option in the View menu.
- Click on AutoShapes, then Callouts.
- Choose a callout shape, e.g. one from the top row with a pointer.
- Click on the screen near the photo and draw out a shape.
- Write text in the callout shape.
- Adjust the pointer by clicking on the handle at its point.
- Move the pointer until it points to a feature on the photo.

If part of the callout goes under the photo, click on its box with the right mouse button and choose Order, then Bring to Front.

Teaching idea

Use an interesting photo as a starter activity. Ask the students a question about it to see if they can suggest any answers. The question can be worded in a way that creates a mystery, for example:

- Why is this goat up a tree?
- Why is the dog wearing goggles?
- How did this car get there?
- Why are these people running?
- Where did this man get his hat?

The answer to the question should open up a wider geographical idea and topic.

Technique tip

You can create a hotspot on a photo in Word. This can act as a hyperlink to another photo, to a map or to text. The link can be to a different file or to a bookmarked place in the same file. These steps show how to make a link from a hotspot on one photo to another photo at a bookmarked place in the same file:

- First, insert the starting map or photo into a Word document.
- Scroll down to a space where you can insert another photo, text or a map, then insert another photo.
- Click on the photo, then click on Insert and Bookmark. Name your bookmark and click on Add.
- Scroll back to the starting photo.
- Choose a rectangle from the Drawing toolbar and draw a rectangle over a place in the photo where you want to create a hotspot.
- Click on the rectangle.
- Click on the Hyperlink icon and choose Bookmark.
- Click on the bookmark name, then click on OK.

You can now click on the hyperlink rectangle to jump to the second photo.

You can hide hotspots by making sure that the rectangle is a 'No fill' (no colour) shape and there is 'No line' around the rectangle. If you want to do this, you must do it before you create the hyperlink.

Teaching idea

Give the students two photos to compare and contrast. To do this, they should:

- list what the photos have in common, e.g. landform or human features
- list the main differences between the common features, e.g. their size and shape
- identify some features that each photo has that the other does not have.

Teaching idea

Photo interpretation can be done by using a template such as the Development Compass Rose or another structure. Students can write in text boxes or callouts (from the AutoShapes menu) around a photo that has been inserted into Word or PowerPoint:

- natural
- economic
- social
- who decides?

This could also be done using mind-mapping software on an interactive whiteboard. Different layers of information can be created and either shown or hidden as required.

Photo hotspots

Another idea is to create hyperlinks to photos from either a photo or a map by means of hotspots. This can be done using nothing more than a word processor such as Word. The effect can be to access more detailed photos from a more general photo that acts as a starting point. The same can be done from a map or from a vertical air photo. In either case, the technique for doing this is the same and the results are equally effective.

Editing digital photos

Digital photos can be edited in a variety of ways for different purposes. They can be cropped to make a better composition, or so that something that is important is deliberately left out. There is, for example, often a question as to what is on either side of a photo. Students could first be shown a cropped photo and asked to think about what is happening nearby. The uncropped photo could then be shown.

Photo editing can also be used to create different landscapes – for example, to show a 'before' and an 'after' effect. This could be to show how a landform has changed over time and what it might look like in the future. The same could be done to show how human features could change a landscape, such as the visual effect of building wind turbines in a countryside area. There is nothing new in the idea of creating and editing images for political or other reasons. Paintings have always been more than a capture of realism, and

Figure 6.4 *Photos can be edited to show change, either recreating a past scene or showing what the scene might look like in the future. All these photos were edited in MS Paint by cutting and pasting parts of one photo onto another. The photo with houses shows what the landscape might look like after more houses have been built; the new houses have been added in, and some parts have been enlarged and rotated to create a realistic effect.*

The other two photos show how a landscape has changed since wind turbines have been built; the turbines have been edited out.

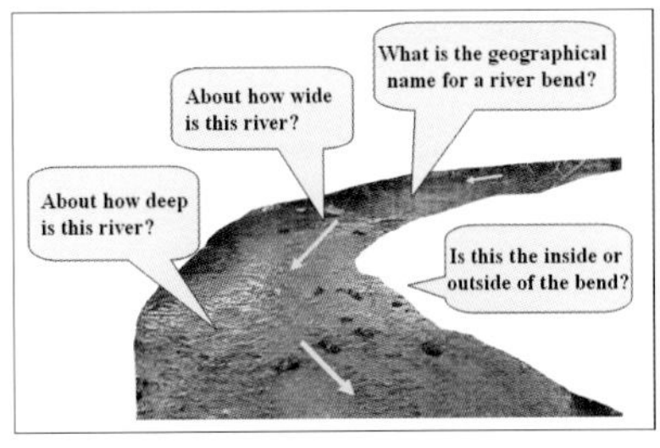

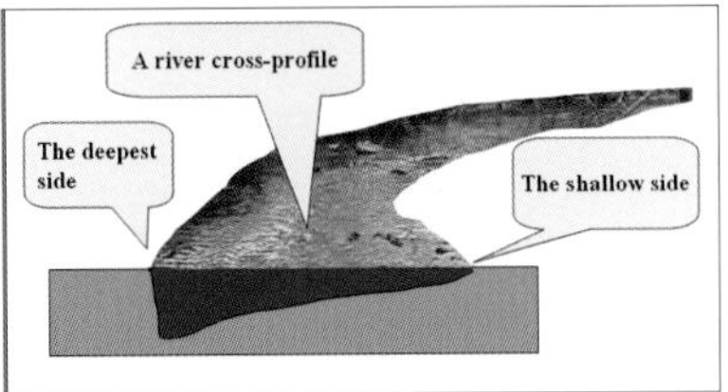

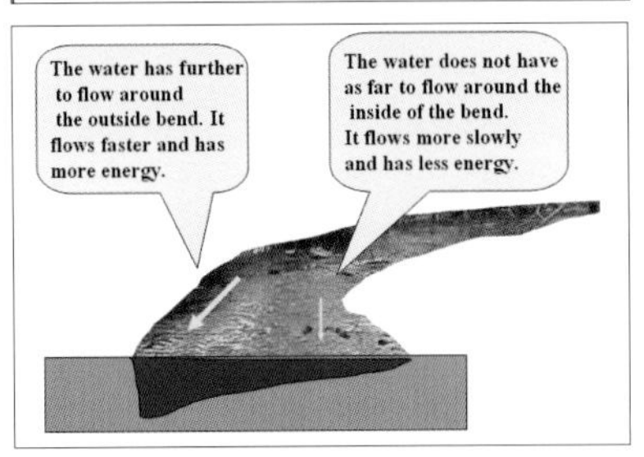

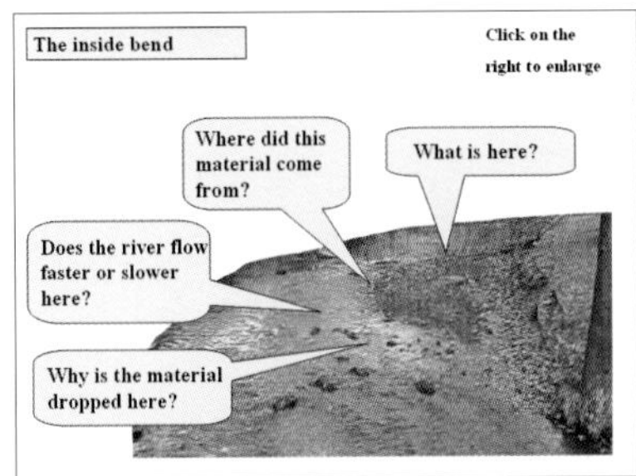

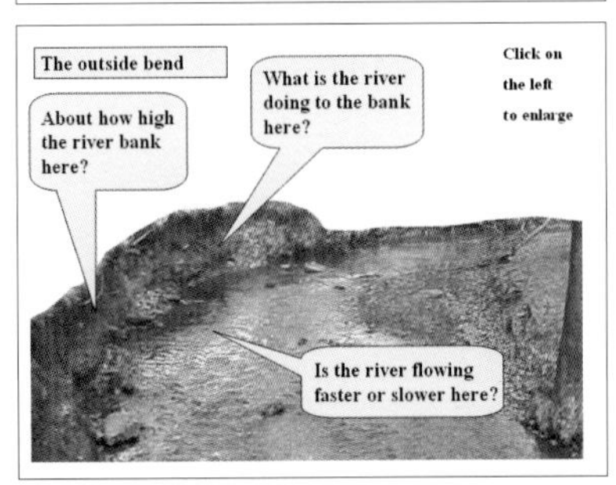

Figure 6.5 *Photos can be inserted into PowerPoint, then parts can be covered over on a set of slides using shapes from the drawing tools. The image can then be revealed in response to students' questions, one slide at a time, until the whole image is revealed.*

photos have been edited since the invention of the airbrush. People have been removed and other changes have been made to give the lie to the phrase 'a photo never lies!'

There is limited use for this in geography, though where perceptions of an area need to be created, it is a technique that students could try out for themselves. They could, for example, create some advertising material for a place that showed its most attractive features by selectively removing what is not so attractive. In geography, this could be used as an activity for developing their critical awareness and visual literacy. It is, after all, a technique that is used to create illusions of place in resources that they may be using in their geography work. This may be in the context of leisure and tourism, or of advertising an area as a location for economic activities.

One thought-provoking activity is to present students with one part of a photo at a time. This could be to give clues for them to work out about a type of landform, a place, an event or a process. They can extract evidence from each piece of the photo as it is revealed, often making guesses by applying previous knowledge. An easy way to do this is in PowerPoint, though it could also be done using other programs. This is done by using shapes from the Drawing tools to cover up most of the photo at the start, then gradually uncovering more of the photo as each slide progresses. The spotlight tool in SMART Tools is a visually interesting way to focus the students' attention on one part of a photo at a time. The spotlight can be progressively enlarged until the full scene is shown. Some of the evidence from a limited part of a photo may take the students down some cul de sacs, but it will certainly force them to look at the photo in great detail.

Line drawings from photos

Photos show detail that may not be needed. A simple line drawing can pick out key features in a way that highlights what is important. A freehand pencil sketch of a photo is one option for creating a line drawing from a photo. It is also possible to use ICT tools to achieve the same result. As with any form of drawing by mouse or touchpad, it requires some practice before an acceptable result can be achieved. Using a PC tablet as a sketch pad has the advantages of both methods. There are also other drawing pads that can produce digital images from freehand drawings. One of these, named DigiMemo, is described in Chapter 8.

One way to create a line drawing from a photo is to use the drawing tools in a word processor. For teachers, this is a relatively simple way to create an accurate line drawing that can be inserted into a worksheet or a presentation. For students, it can help those who are unable to draw perspective and outlines with any degree of accuracy.

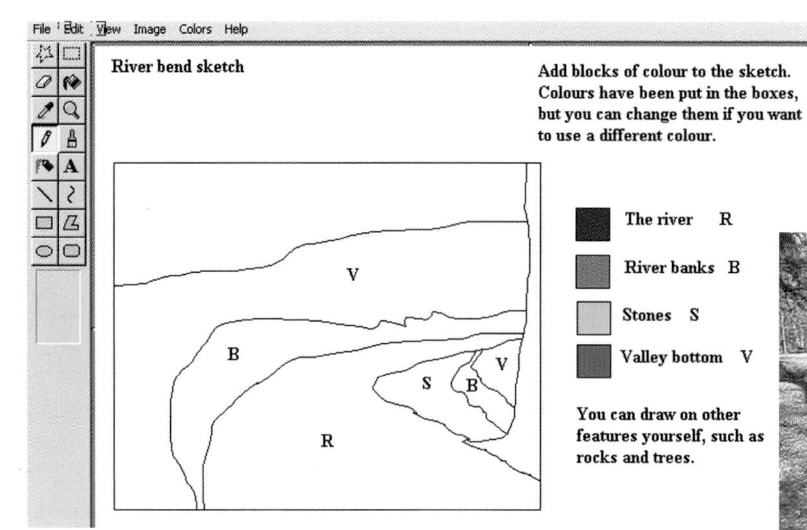

Figure 6.6 *A line drawing can be made from a photo in Word, then inserted into MS Paint, where students can work with it – for example, using colours to shade the main landform features and adding labels.*

Teaching idea

Provide students with a photo of a landform or a landscape scene.
Get them to edit the photo by adding a new feature to it or removing an existing feature. Some examples might include:

- removing a meander bend from an oblique air photo
- covering part of a landscape with forest
- building a wind turbine on a hill
- removing electricity pylons and power cables from a landscape.

For physical features, they should then explain the processes that have changed the scene. For human features, they should give their ideas as to whether they have improved or spoilt the landscape.

Technique tip

You can crop a photo in a Word or PowerPoint document after you have inserted it:

- Click on the photo.
- Open the Picture toolbar if it does not automatically appear.
- Click on the Crop tool.
- Place the tool over the middle handle on one edge of the photo, then click.
- Crop the photo by dragging the side of the photo inwards.

Artistic effects

Most drawing and photo editing programs have tools that can change a photo to give it different kinds of effects, including different shapes. A photo can be made to look like a watercolour, an impressionist painting, a sketched line drawing or incorporate other effects. Its shape can be changed to a cylinder, a circle or other distortions. There may be some ways in which these effects can be used in geography. It may, for example, be valid to make use of these distortions if direct links are being made to work in art, and if the students are being encouraged to create their own impressions of landscapes. This may help them to understand how landscapes can create moods and feelings as well as geographical information. Distorting an image may also be a way of generating some initial interest in a scene. The danger is that these effects may be used for no other reason other than because the tools exist and it can be done.

Technique tip

You can reveal small parts of a photo at a time to see if the students can work out what the photo shows and to ask questions about it.

- Open PowerPoint and start a new presentation with a blank slide template.
- Insert one photo on the slide.
- Use the rectangle drawing tool to draw over parts of the photo you want to hide. You can draw several shapes on the same photo. Click on the White Fill colour and No line options to make the hidden areas blend in with the background. If the slide background colour is not white, choose a different Fill colour to match it.
- Go to the Slide Sorter view, then copy and paste the same image once.
- Click on the rectangle you have drawn and drag back part of it to reveal some more of the photo.
- Copy and paste this slide, and repeat until the whole photo has been revealed.

Technique tip

How to use the Drawing tools in Word to create a line drawing:

- Insert a photo into the Word document.
- Select the rectangle tool and draw a frame around the photo.
- Change the infill from white to No fill.
- Use the Freeform drawing tool from the AutoShapes menu to draw individual lines on the photo; each line is a separate editable object.
- When you have finished, click on the photo and delete it; make sure not to delete your lines instead of the photo.
- Click on Draw then Group to group all the separate objects.

Teaching idea

This activity could be done using a drawing program such as Paint or Paint Shop Pro.

- Provide the students with a photo of a scene that shows a landscape that tourists might like to visit.
- Get the students to use image processing tools to create a different perception of the scene by using the image processing tools, e.g. to show it as a watercolour or oil painting.
- Discuss how effective the new image might be in attracting visitors and how it compares to the unedited photo.

Stitched-up photos

The panorama effect in which photos show a complete circle around the landscape can be a powerful visual aid to help students feel that they are standing there. When the display is shown on a big screen, one can look around the total scene, except it is a scene that is moving. There are several programs in which this can be done relatively easily. It involves standing in a central position, then taking a set of photos in a circle with a small amount of overlap between them. The program does the rest by merging them as seamlessly as it can. This works well, for example, for looking at a village, a landform, a shopping centre or any type of place that can benefit from being seen in panorama. Controls in the program allow the user to move around in either direction, zoom in and also look up and down. This gives the students some degree of 'hands on' interaction.

Websites with panorama scenes can be found by using 'panorama' as a search word. Some CD-Roms such as Encarta contain similar scenes. The use of panorama photos may be the nearest one can get to the virtual field visit.

Webcams

Webcams take photos that are updated at regular intervals, sometimes several times each minute. It is, for example, possible to watch traffic on a motorway, the view from a volcano or animals in game reserve coming to a waterhole. These bring an almost real-time dimension to work in geography that is impossible to replicate in other ways. A clock and date show that the events are happening as the students watch. This brings an air of realism to students who, from their classroom in the UK, can watch the almost real-time action taking place in a South African game reserve as a herd of elephants comes down to the waterhole. Nobody can know what will happen next since it has never been seen before.

Time for the movies

The home digital video has arrived and is increasingly affordable. Even the problems of file size are being overcome as computers are fitted with rewritable DVD hardware and hard drive disk space increases. There are also websites from which digital movies can be downloaded.

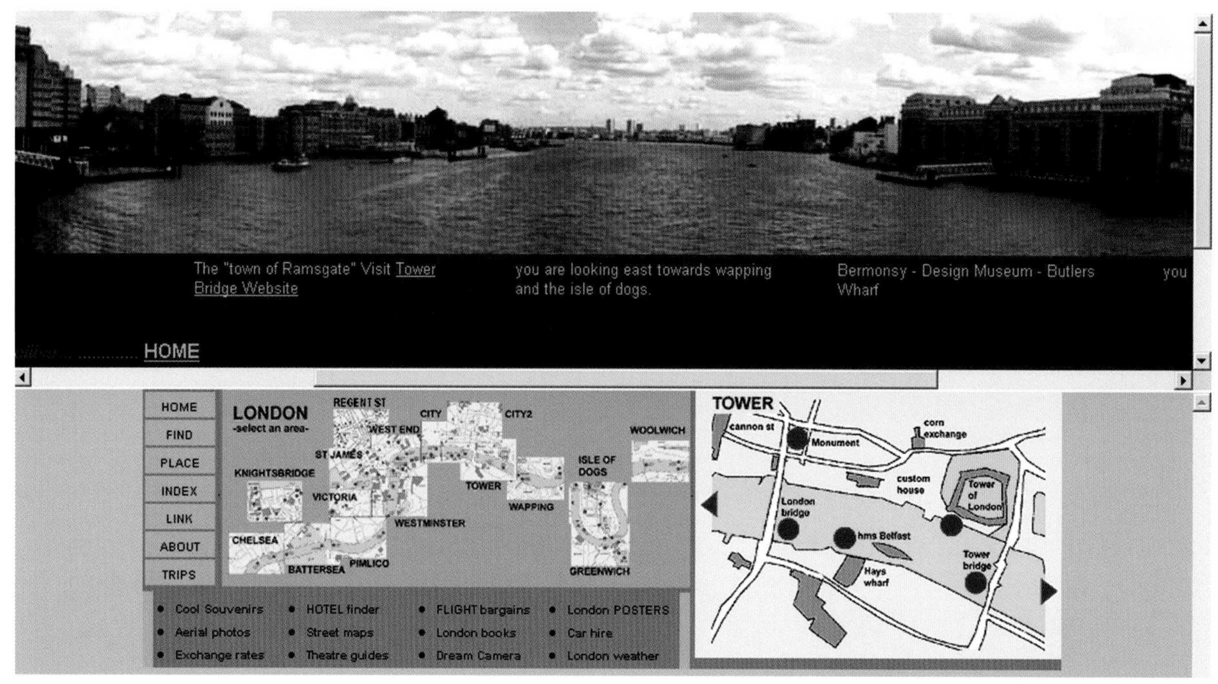

Figure 6.7 *Panorama images show a scene in a full circle. They can be controlled by the user to give an element of interactivity and engagement. They are easy to create using panorama software.*

© Explore London

Teaching idea

There are many panorama images on websites. These include a panoramic view from the top of Mount Everest, the view from the top of Mount St Helens volcano, a view of the harbour at St Ives in Cornwall and many others. It can be worth finding a panorama site for a place or topic the students are studying by using the keyword 'panorama' in a web search. If the image is set to run automatically, this could make an interesting starter activity for a lesson. It could also be used with a map to give practice in using compass points.

Websites

ExploreLondon
Virtual London
VR London
The World Wide Panorama
World map with sites
Easypano
Panorama software available in various trial versions

Digital video can be used in several ways – for example, as a form of presentation in its own right, or as a short clip for insertion into another ICT application such as a multi-media authoring program. The seamless integration of a short movie clip to show a process in action, a short interview or perhaps just panning around a scene, can help to present an idea effectively. Another likely benefit of a short clip is its ability to keep the students' attention. Still images can be taken from a movie using DVD

Teaching idea

Get the students to use webcams to compare different places. The topic could be to compare traffic flows, the weather or other aspects of the landscape. Some webcams allow you to access archive images. Some give control over which camera to use in a location.

Websites
Camscape
EarthCam
Global Geografia

software. Digital video also has the facility for moving to bookmarked places – something that is difficult to achieve with analogue video.

The geographical activity of writing a script for a film, or conducting an interview, can at last move away from being a pretend, paper-based activity to one that is real. The students themselves, or perhaps the teacher, could become part of the movie. There can surely be nothing more motivating than for students to know that the work they do will be shown to an audience, even if the audience is in their own classroom.

Wider issues with digital images

Digital photos offer opportunities for teaching that go beyond what can realistically be done without ICT. The variety of photos, and the ways in which they can be edited, create opportunities for the effective teaching and learning of 'good' geography. As with other aspects of ICT, the use of digital photos has the potential to transform the subject, not only in how it is taught and learnt, but also in some of the new dimensions of geography that it can offer.

Projector power

Using digital photos, as with 35-mm transparencies, depends on having the right kind of classroom equipment and fittings. In particular, it is best if the images can be projected onto a matt white screen in a darkened room. Unfortunately, even these basic conditions are too often not available in the geography classroom. White or light-coloured blinds are often the problem. This happens when the decision of decor is taken by someone whose main concerns are for cost and a matching colour scheme with the walls, rather than for the practical need for a blackout. Thin, light-coloured curtains create a similar problem. Lack of money for constant repairs affects both. The effect of sunlight streaming through skylights, curtains and gaps in blinds can be enough to ruin the impact of an awesome landscape. The problem can be compounded by the use of a shiny-surfaced whiteboard that reflects the light back off the screen. Some interactive whiteboards also have this problem, but

Figure 6.8 *There are many sources of digital movie clips on websites and other sources. This example is a movie on DVD about the High Arctic area. Another approach is to use a digital movie for a commercial film.* The Day after Tomorrow, *for example, could be used to introduce students to ideas about global warming.*

Teaching idea

Get students to write their own commentary over a video news report or some other short video clip. They could be provided with some basic facts about the event using text material.

Websites

BBC News
Major news events often have video clips.
British Film Institute: Education: Secondary Teaching resources
BBC: GCSC Geography
Video clips

many do not. Fortunately, a good data projector can do much to compensate for poor blackout conditions, though even a data projector gives best results in a dark room.

The interactive whiteboard

An interactive whiteboard linked to a data projector and computer offers opportunities for involving students directly in a presentation that includes photos. Students can be asked to come to the board and write notes or labels on photos. Their handwritten notes can be changed into print and made clearer so that everyone can read them. They can move parts of a photo around the screen to drag and drop the parts together. Indeed, any kind of image editing can be done on the interactive whiteboard, using the mouse and keyboard with on-screen touch commands. In SMART Notebook, notes and images from the lesson can be saved as a PDF file and made available on a departmental website.

Developing visual literacy

Photos in geography are more than a means of allowing visual learners to access the subject. They are an essential part of the information system that adds to the students' understanding of landscape and the processes that shape it. The ability to interpret photos, whether ground views, oblique views or vertical air views, is an essential skill in the subject. It is an aspect of visual literacy that to its detriment has received only limited attention in National Curriculum thinking and in the Secondary (KS3) Strategy guidance materials.

There is no 'reading age' for photos. It would, however, be wrong to assume that, because the medium is entirely visual, the photo will somehow speak for itself. Teachers of geography know that this is not true. Photos need to be studied in detail and interpreted for meaning. It could even be argued that the clues are less obvious than with text, making them even harder to spot. The development of a 'geographical eye' that will help students to interpret photos is something that should be one of the success criteria for work in geography.

The different ways of working with digital photos provide enormous scope for the students to develop a deep understanding of how photos can be used to provide information. They can engage in photo editing and other activities to explore whether the information contained in photos is likely to be balanced, deliberately distorted or even plainly untrue. It is also possible to explore different ways of 'seeing' a landscape, for example, from more artistic perspectives. Not everyone 'sees' landscapes through the technical eye of a geographer, and it is important to appreciate that different approaches can be equally valid.

Technology take-over

The use of ICT always raises questions about the extent to which the technology is in danger of taking over from the geography. The example of an activity to create a digital video of a landform or some other topic illustrates this problem. It is partly a problem of time – for example, the time that it takes for students to learn how to use the hardware and software, and the time that it takes to create a finished product.

The NC Orders for Geography do refer to communicating with an audience in different ways as part of geographical enquiry and as a skill. There will, however, be a point at which the skill of communicating becomes so dominant that it takes over from the geographical content. There may be other valid reasons why time spent on presentation and communication is justified – for example, to include kinaesthetic teaching and learning strategies as part of the general repertoire. But there must be a point at which the geography teacher stops to consider whether the subject itself is becoming nothing other than a context for the ICT.

There is certainly a case for making use of a range of relatively simple ICT techniques that the students should be taught as part of their ICT-specific work. These involve simple photo editing, using images in different formats and copying and pasting or inserting photos into different ICT applications.

They may even be able to transfer ICT techniques learnt in art lessons, such as the ability to work with a photo editing or drawing program.

It is a matter of getting the balance right so that the time needed to learn new ICT techniques is justified by the gains to be made from good-quality geography. This involves doing traditional things in new ways, as well as moving into dimensions that are only possible by the use of ICT.

Digital images and the law

Digital images of students, whether they be stills or movies, need to be taken in accordance with the law. This is to remove any possibility, no matter how remote, that images of the students could be used in pornographic or other illegal ways. Permission needs to be sought from parents, especially if the images are to be used in any public domain site such as on the school website. As with most laws, interpreting the contexts for what is legal and what is not is seldom straightforward. It is, therefore, a matter that teachers need to check carefully in case of any inadvertent infringement.

Check it out

Think about the work you do with your students on photo interpretation.

What features of a photo might make it easier or more difficult for students to interpret it? Think about:

- the use of colour
- the size of the photo
- the number of features
- the amount of detail
- the clarity of the outlines
- the angle of viewing.

How might you achieve progression in the students' ability to describe and interpret photos?

Chapter 7 Processes in action

Key questions

- What criteria can be used to assess quality in students' understanding of geographical processes?
- Which geographical concepts and processes can ICT help students to understand?
- How does a study of geographical processes using ICT link to the NC Orders for ICT?
- How can different ICT applications help to bring about a greater understanding of geographical processes?
- What limitations are there to using ICT to illustrate geographical processes?

ICT applications

- MS Paint
- Web browser
- Flash animation
- Morphing software
- PowerPoint

Focus on processes

The question of how things work is central to developing an understanding of geography. This is the question that leads to studying processes – a word that encompasses everything from the physical processes that create a beach to the human processes involved in decisions over how farmers use their land.

A problem with studying physical processes is that geography, as taught in schools, is not traditionally a laboratory-based subject. Usually the only equipment to be found is a sink and some electricity sockets. Some schools do have hardware models, such as a working model of a coastal or river environment, but these are the exception. Sometimes, it is the scale of physical processes in geography that causes the problem. Timescale and sheer physical size are often impossible for students to comprehend when they are only able to see landscape processes drawn in books or as sketches on a whiteboard. It is also difficult to appreciate how different parts of the process are linked when still images and text are all that is available. The use of ICT cannot resolve all these problems, but it can often help students to develop a better understanding of how some physical processes work.

Studying human processes is even more problematic. This is the area of decision making where values and viewpoints play a part. But as well as values and viewpoints, decision makers usually use data to underpin their conclusions, even though the data may be selectively chosen. The data may also be selectively processed and presented. Part of the decision-making process can involve a form of modelling by asking the 'what if?' question. What, for example, would happen to the viability of a location for an industrial

Check it out

Think about how you help your students to understand processes in geography:

- What methods are you currently able to use to show movement and links between processes? Are you, for example, able to show animations, and can you model change?
- Do you use any physical models to show processes, e.g. a landform model with running water?
- Do you use any experiments to show physical processes, e.g. to demonstrate erosion by moving ice?
- To what extent do your students have problems in understanding the scale of physical processes and the complex ways in which processes are linked?
- Do you engage your students in any decision-making games or simulations? Do they involve making calculations and does this cause any problems?
- Are there any ways in which you already use ICT to demonstrate geographical processes to your students?
- Do you give your students any opportunities to use ICT to engage them in modelling processes for themselves?

Making links

NC Orders for Geography: KS3 PoS

Knowledge and understanding of patterns and processes

Pupils should be taught to:

- describe and explain patterns of physical and human features and relate these to the character of places and environments
- identify, describe and explain physical and human processes, and their impact on places and environments.

activity if the costs of transport were to change? One way to answer this question is to set up a mathematical model so that variables can be changed, even where pure economics may not be the deciding factor. Where figures are involved, the use of ICT is likely to be of benefit. Some of these ideas link across to Chapter 5.

Making links

NC Orders: Thinking Skills

Information-processing skills enable pupils to:
- understand relationships, e.g. part/whole relationships.

Enquiry skills enable pupils to:
- predict outcomes, test conclusions and improve ideas.

Reasoning skills enable pupils to:
- draw inferences and make deductions
- make judgements and decisions informed by reasons or evidence.

Creative thinking skills enable pupils to:
- generate and extend ideas
- suggest possible hypotheses
- be imaginative in their thinking
- look for alternative innovative outcomes.

Quality in understanding geographical processes

The Level Descriptions (Attainment Targets) in the NC Orders for Geography give general guidance for identifying and assessing quality and progression in a student's understanding of geographical processes. Although these criteria only apply to key stages 1–3, the higher levels overlap with what can be expected at key stage 4. The Orders contain an expectation that higher levels of understanding will be characterised by:

- a more detailed description of the processes
- use of more specialist geographical vocabulary
- a deeper understanding of the links and relationships that exist between processes, including ways in which human and physical processes can interact.

The time dimension

Time is a difficult concept for students to understand properly in geography. This is partly because it works at so many different scales, from 'real time' through to geological time. The latter is counted in hundreds of millions of years – a scale that is completely inconceivable to most people. This kind of timescale must be accepted in the abstract, with figures serving simply as an index of a sequence of events. Yet it is essential for the students to have

Figure 7.1 *These images combine a program named Stress Relief with a photo shown in MS Paint. The hammer strikes the coast, making a breaking sound, while the chainsaw wears it away. The program also simulates a machine gun and other devices that can be used to show erosion processes.*

The program can be downloaded for free from the Gemtree website

Making links

NC Orders for Geography: Attainment Targets

Level 4
They recognise and describe physical and human processes. They recognise and describe physical and human processes. They begin to understand how these can change the features of places, and how these changes affect the lives and activities of people living there.

Level 5
They describe and begin to explain geographical patterns and physical and human processes. They describe how these processes can lead to similarities and differences in the environments of different places and in the lives of people who live there.

Level 6
They describe and explain a range of physical and human processes and recognise that these processes interact to produce the distinctive characteristics of places. They describe ways in which physical and human processes operating at different scales create geographical patterns and lead to changes in places.

Level 7
They describe interactions within and between physical and human processes, and show how these interactions create geographical patterns and help change places and environments.

some grasp of timescales in order to understand geographical processes. For example, cliff erosion in some parts of the UK is taking place within a timescale that is easy to understand – sometimes you can actually even see it happening. But in other places where rocks are more resistant, the rate of erosion is very much slower. So while in some places it may be extremely unwise to build a house near the coast, in other places there would be little risk over the next thousand years. A student who can grasp this concept is likely to have a better understanding of geographical processes than one for whom these multiple time dimensions serve only to confuse.

Forward to the future

The future is another aspect of the time dimension that is important for work in geography. Any kind of planning involves looking to the future, though the timescale used for taking planning decisions can often to be relatively limited. Students need to be able to think about the implications of decision-making for the future. This also requires an understanding of how a sequence of events can be set in motion, such as the melting of the Arctic sea ice and the danger that it could trigger changes in the flow of the North Atlantic Drift. On a more immediate future timescale, a new building or structure in the landscape will have an immediate and largely predictable effect on its appearance. So one criterion of quality in understanding processes should relate to the ability not only to describe what has happened in the past, but also to apply that information to future scenarios.

24 hr European satellite animation

This European satellite animation uses infrared heat analysis to display 'clouds' and combines four images taken at six hour intervals during the last 24 hours. It is updated every six hours.

Figure 7.2 *Animations of weather patterns can be run to show how the weather has changed over the last few days. Animations can also run predictions of processes into the future.*

Processes and size

It is hard for students to imagine that the top of Snowdon was once at the bottom of a syncline, or that the top of Everest is formed from rocks that were once beneath an ocean. There is a time dimension to understanding what has happened, but there is also a question of the sheer scale of the area and heights that have been involved. Landforms on this kind of scale are hard to comprehend, especially when presented as maps in an atlas or photos in a textbook. At the other end of the scale, geographers can study how water permeates through pores in soil, or how hydraulic action works to open cracks in a rock. Although nothing can replace the real experience of visiting a place, there are some ways in which the use of ICT can help to bridge this conceptual gap in scales.

The idea of fractals adds an interesting angle to work in geography. Fractals involve the repetition of mathematical objects or sets to produce patterns at a multiplicity of scales, and some natural processes and patterns show small- and large-scale similarities that are in some ways analogous to fractals. It might, for example, be useful to think of the small-scale meandering patterns on a beach as water flows back to the sea, and to compare this with the meanders of a river system such as the Amazon. This is a situation in which an understanding of the scales at which processes work is fundamental to understanding how things happen.

An understanding of processes in human geography is equally problematic when students lack a real feeling for scale, or at least a good conceptual grasp of it. Cities of more than ten million people that sprawl out over the landscape are hard to visualise or comprehend. Students may live in a city of which they have only partial knowledge and little real understanding in terms of size. The process of globalisation is a case where the size and distribution of an operation is, by definition, global in its extent.

Whether human or physical processes are involved, it is important for students to develop a sense of scale in relation to the size of what they are studying. Without this sense, there is ample opportunity for misconceptions and confusion.

Links between processes

The Level Descriptions for the NC Orders for Geography are clear in identifying links between processes as one of the criteria that define higher levels of achievement. Perhaps this is an aspect of geography where the subject parts company with the scientific approach that is possible in a laboratory. Laboratory experiments to test hypotheses and study processes tend to focus on one variable at a time, making every effort to hold other variables constant. The essence of geography, however, is to take a more holistic approach in an attempt to understand the complexity of the links. Simple systems diagrams are useful to show how one part of a process works, but systems that create landscapes and patterns of climate are far more complex. Inputs, stores and outputs need to be tracked over different scales of time and space.

Links between human processes can be even more complex. The concept of interdependence is now an important one to study because of the growing realisation that decisions in one part of the world can have effects elsewhere.

Making links

NC Orders for Citizenship: Attainment Targets

Pupils have a broad knowledge and understanding of the topical events they study; the rights, responsibilities and duties of citizens; the role of the voluntary sector; forms of government; provision of public services; and the criminal and legal systems. They show how the public gets information and how opinion is formed and expressed, including through the media. They show understanding of how and why changes take place in society. Pupils take part in school and community-based activities, demonstrating personal and group responsibility in their attitudes to themselves and others.

It is difficult, for example, to understand that smoking a cigarette or eating a hamburger can affect an area of tropical rain forest or the composition of the Earth's atmosphere. The phrases 'act locally and think globally' and 'the global village' help to sum up the complex scales and interactions of these links. A better understanding of geography will involve a better understanding of this complexity. It is important to consider the part that ICT can play in demonstrating this complexity.

Teaching idea

Students can discover the ways in which their own actions can play a part in affecting the environment by completing an online survey. This can help them to understand the complexity of the links between physical and human processes, as well as the part that their own actions play in wider global processes.

Website

Global Footprints: How big is your footprint?
An interactive quiz

Applying skills and knowledge

A thorough understanding of processes is needed for students to apply their knowledge. This can involve making decisions that are run in a mathematical model or as a simulation. Students could, for example, be presented with a case study where a coastline is being eroded and where defences need to be built. They could apply their knowledge of coastal defence techniques to the problem, making predictions as to how successful their solutions might be. In human geography, they could make decisions about running a farm, locating a hypermarket or managing a country's economy.

The quality of their understanding of processes can be revealed by the ways in which they apply their knowledge and understanding of data, information and viewpoints to make decisions. Their depth of understanding can be

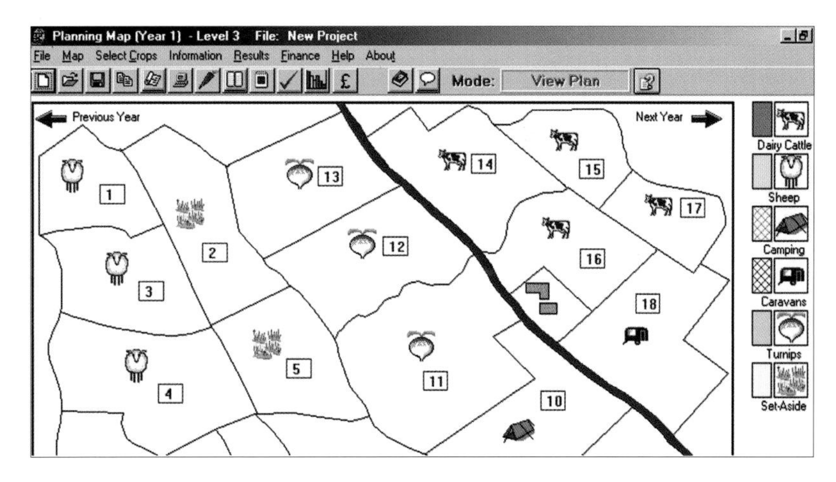

Figure 7.3 *Decision-making activities such as this farm simulation can be run either independently by one student or as a small-group activity in which the students discuss their decisions collaboratively.*

© Geopacks 08705 133168

revealed by their attention to detail and the extent to which they identify causal links between the processes. Correlation statistics can be used to demonstrate statistical relationships. A more developed understanding would then go on to show exactly how the links between the processes function. There are several aspects of modelling and simulation where the use of ICT can be of benefit. Indeed, it is likely that some of this kind of work cannot realistically be done without the use of ICT.

Using ICT for geographical processes

In this section, the aim is to focus on ways in which different ICT applications can play a part in developing an understanding of the following aspects of processes:

- scale, measured in terms of area, distance or height – using a big screen
- how processes work – using diagrams and photo editing
- change over time – using animation and morphing
- links between processes – using mind mapping, modelling and simulation.

It is obvious from the outset that these are not discrete headings. The processes invariably work over a period of time, and there are bound to be links between processes. The headings, however, can serve as a means of identifying the various ICT applications and techniques so that we can focus on each in turn.

Making links

NC Orders for ICT: KS3 PoS

Developing ideas and making things happen
Pupils should be taught:

- to develop and explore information, solve problems and derive new information for particular purposes
- how to use ICT to test predictions and discover patterns and relationships, by exploring, evaluating and developing models and changing their rules and values.

Scale on the big screen

It must first be stated that nothing can replace the reality of a field visit in its power to demonstrate the scale of some landforms and the processes that form them. However, digital images projected onto a large screen can do more to create a sense of scale than images in a textbook. The full colour impact can also help to develop this sense of scale. Images can be projected through any drawing or photo-processing software, either directly onto a screen or onto an interactive whiteboard. Further ideas about the use of photos and other images are presented in Chapter 6.

The big screen, perhaps perversely, can also be an effective way of showing features and processes that are normally too small to be seen clearly. Without a microscope, students in a geography lesson will still be able to see what is happening at the microscopic end of the scale.

One way to demonstrate scale is to present a series of images in succession, each showing how the subsequent image nests within a larger-scale image. To take a simple example, a set of images could be taken of a landscape that progressively zoom in on a feature such as a volcano. From an oblique or vertical air view, perhaps even using satellite imagery, a series of images could

Technique tip

The SMART tools for the SMART interactive whiteboard include a recording tool for making a movie. Once set to record, the tool makes a movie of everything that happens on-screen. You can use it to create a movie that shows how to zoom into a landscape. The file is saved in AVI format. This means it can be imported into many types of software for use on an interactive whiteboard, for example. You may also find this tool useful for creating short movies of sequences of actions for work within a program. Be warned, however, that saving even short movies in this format can take up a lot of disk space.

zoom in to reveal its details down to individual lava flows and rocks. This helps to keep each part of the feature in its proper context. The Google Earth program allows students to begin with a view of the Earth, then to zoom down to local scales. The same kind of effect can be achieved by using the *Multimap* website.

Teaching idea

As a starter activity, show the students a close-up view of a feature – for example, some ripples in sand on a beach or a rocky surface. See if they can work out whether they are looking at a full-size feature or a close-up image. You will need to choose the photo carefully so that the scale is not obvious. Identify the features of the scene.

Teaching idea

Use the *Window on the UK 2000* CD-Rom, either by showing it or by letting the students work with it themselves. This CD-Rom has a tool that allows the user to zoom in on a scene. This is especially effective when used with the bank of oblique air photos.

Notice that, although the image itself remains the same, the zoom tool lets you see more of the detail in the image. By zooming into maximum scale, it is usually possible to see details such as cars and even people. This may give students a better understanding of the scale of the larger image.

Processes in diagrams

Processes in geography are often most easily shown by simplified drawings that remove the detail of each location in order to concentrate on how the process is working. One might, for example might be to show how a waterfall is retreating, showing the features by means of two or more 2D or 3D diagrams. Diagrams can be drawn in MS Paint or in another simple drawing program. Apart from their technical neatness, ICT makes it easy to edit and move them into another application such as PowerPoint or Word. For students, the drawing tools and colour palette ensure that they are able to draw something that is clear to look at and for which no particular artistic skills are needed. If they cannot do that, then clip art images are usually available, either from websites or from the galleries in interactive whiteboard software.

Animated processes

Processes are by their very nature dynamic. This dynamic aspect can be shown simply in a program such as PowerPoint. The drawing tools can be used to draw arrows. The arrows can then be animated to show how and when something happens. This can be done by selecting when, where and how the arrows appear on the screen.

Teaching idea

Get the students to draw block diagrams to show the different types of valley shapes, such as a narrow V-shaped valley with a steep gradient, or a broad valley with gentle slopes and a shallow gradient. They can do this in MS Paint or another drawing program. They should add labels and notes to show what they have drawn.

Emphasise that neatness and clarity are important when drawing a diagram, so they should make full use of the program's tools – drawing straight lines for the base and using the freeform drawing tool, the text tool and the colour palette.

Editing change over time

Processes operate over different timescales. When it is not possible to get 'before' and 'after' photos, a digital image can be edited to show possible changes. You can do this by using any photo-editing or drawing program. Even MS Paint can be used to import a JPG photo image and change it. The technique involves little more than the ability to copy and paste. Some additional 'touching up' can be done by using the program's basic drawing tools, such as the spray and colour match tools. These techniques are described in Chapter 6.

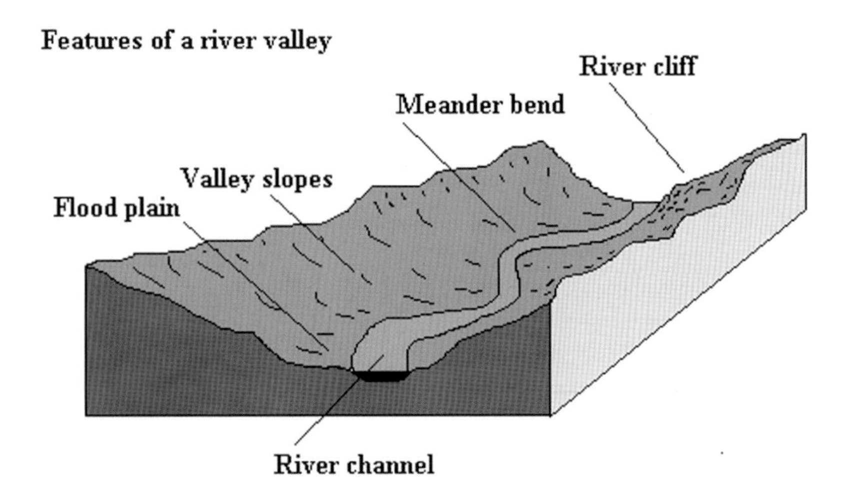

Figure 7.4 *Block diagrams or 2D diagrams can be drawn in MS Paint, then used in other applications such as PowerPoint. Diagrams to show stages in landform processes can also be downloaded from websites.*

Teaching idea

Sometimes ICT can even help with the old methods. Students can build a paper model of a volcano using a pattern that has been printed from the USGS or Volcano World website.

Websites

USGS

Volcano World

Binghampton University: Alan L Jones

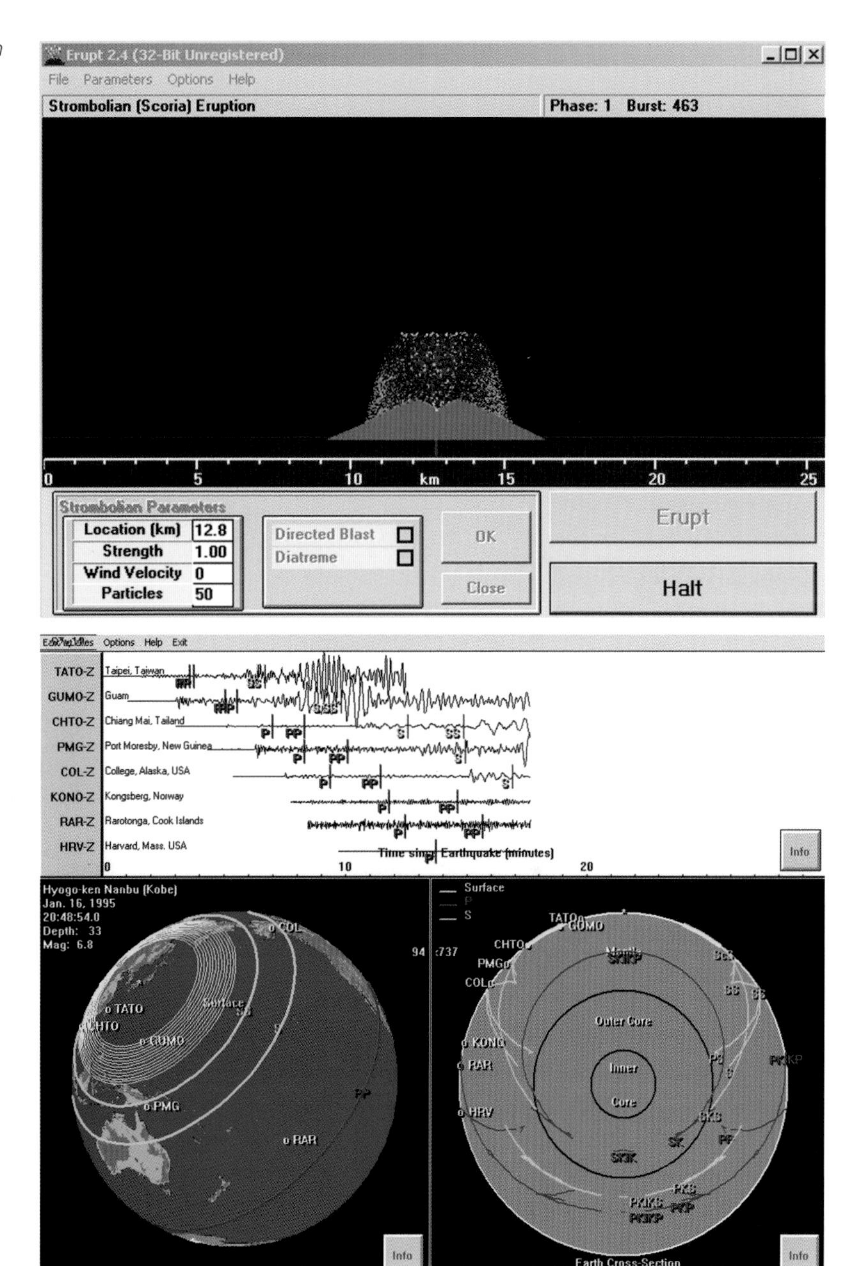

Figure 7.5 *The Seismic/Eruption program allows students to model what might happen when a volcano erupts. Students can choose between different types of eruption and change variables to see what will happen. The program is available as a free download from a website.*

© Alan L Jones

Figure 7.6 *The Seismic Waves program allows students to choose an earthquake and then watch how shock waves move through the Earth's interior. The powerful graphics of the program show the shock waves in different dimensions, including as a graph. The program is available as a free download from a website.*

© Alan L Jones

Teaching idea

The students can use animation software to create their own animations of geographical processes. Some examples can be found on the Hampstead School Geography Department website.

Websites

Hampstead School Geography Department
BBC News: Global Climate Change: Greenhouse Effect

Teaching idea

The geography department at the University of Oregon has created a set of animations to show different aspects of global climate. These can be used to show how world climate patterns change throughout the year. Other websites can be used to show different patterns.

Websites

University of Oregon Department of Geography: Global Climate Animations
The Globe Project: Maps & Graphs: GLOBE Maps
Animated maps and visual animations
Juicy Geography: Animations
Animations of rivers and atmospheric circulation

Teaching idea

Students could provide their own commentaries on animations that show tectonic processes. This could be done as part of a plenary.

Website

USGS: Plate tectonics animations

Technique tip

Create a simple animated image in PowerPoint to show a process at work.

- Choose a photo of a physical feature that is being produced by erosion, such as a valley with a glacier.
- Insert the image onto a blank slide template.
- Draw arrows using the arrow drawing tool in the Drawing toolbar.
- Use the animation effects so that the arrows appear in sequence, showing the movement of the glacier, whether it is advancing or melting back.
- Use callouts from AutoShapes to label the processes at work. The labels can point to where the process takes place.

Real time and simulated change

For some types of change, ICT can provide information about change in 'real time', i.e. as it happens. A webcam, for example, can show the traffic building up on a motorway or weather events in distant locations. For events that take place over a longer timescale, such as the passage of a depression across the UK, a set of images can be combined to run as an animated sequence. This speeds up the process, compressing an event that takes place over three or four days into a clip of several seconds. Some animations can be downloaded from websites, such as an animation showing the movement of the Earth's tectonic plates over millions of years. For a process that is too fast to study clearly, digital images can be shown in a slower sequence. You can repeat any of these animations or slide shows by simply reloading or rerunning the file.

A morphing program provides an interesting alternative to using still images or animations. It enables you to create a simple animation that shows how a landscape can change – for example, a cliff face at different states of erosion. One image can be the starting image. The other is created by editing the image to look as it might appear in the past or in the future. The images are imported into the morphing program and reference points are dotted on both images. The program's engine does the rest. The result is a home-made movie a few seconds long that shows landscape change or how a map can change. The effect may be unrealistic as the program is not likely to show the exact shape of the landscape during the transition. It can, however, provide a visual illusion of change that captures the attention, even if only briefly.

Technique tip

It is easy to edit a photo in MS Paint, though the limitations of the program need to be understood as well as its tools. These steps show how a feature can be changed:

- Open a new screen in Paint. Make sure that the working area takes up most or all of the screen. To do this, you may need to change the image dimensions (Attributes from the Image menu).
- Insert a photo into Paint by using Paste From on the Edit menu.
- Drag the photo to the centre of the page, leaving the top left-hand corner of the screen as a blank space.
- To edit the photo, you can use one part of the photo to mask out another part, e.g. you can edit part of the coast by placing an area of sea over it. Use the Freeform select tool to draw around a shape you want to use as a mask.
- Click on Copy and then on Paste. The part you have copied will appear in the blank space in the top left-hand corner of the screen.
- Check that the Draw Opaque setting in the Image menu is unselected (no tick).
- The copied shape should be already selected, but if not, draw a rectangle around it using the Select tool.
- Drag the shape over the feature you want to mask.
- You can edit the image further by using the Pick Color and the Airbrush tools.

Teaching idea

Edit a photo to show what a landform might look like at different stages. Show the students the photos and see if they can work out the sequence in which the processes have taken place. Examples might include a meander bend that breaks through, a coastal feature or a sequence of cloud formations.

Flash animation is another way to create a simple set of diagrams that show movement and change over time. This can, for example, show the movement of an ice sheet or a glacier as it moves forward, picking up shattered rock and wearing down the landscape. Flash animations can be copied from websites by using a piece of software called Save Flash. Once captured, the animation can then be inserted into PowerPoint, interactive whiteboard software or another program that can handle this file type.

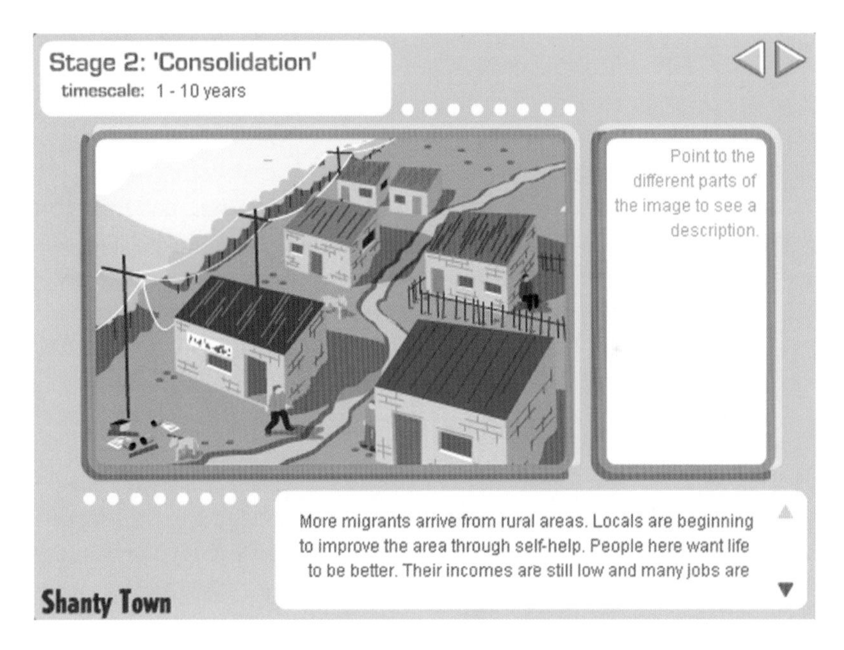

Figure 7.7 *Animations on websites and CD-Roms can give students an understanding of processes at work. Students can also create their own animations using software such as Flash.*

Bob Jones, Alleynes High School, Staffs. Staffordshire Learning Net

Mind mapping and systems diagrams

One key element in progression and higher levels of achievement is the idea that there are links between different geographical processes. They may link physical processes such as flooding, soil erosion, deforestation and climate. They can also link human and physical processes, such as in decisions about how land use planning can affect run-off and river flow. There are few if any entirely closed systems in geography. Teaching the complexity of how processes work is one of the aims of teaching the subject. Mind mapping is one way of showing the links between processes. The layout of a spider diagram or 'knowledge tree' can help to show how processes affect, and are affected by, each other.

Teaching idea

Take a set of screen shots of changing set of events such as the passage of a depression. One way to do this is to use the capture tool in Paint Shop Pro. Place the separate images in a jumbled order on an interactive whiteboard. The students can then come to the front and rearrange the images into their correct order.

Teaching idea

Use a live webcam to study pedestrian or traffic flows in a town.

- Access and study a webcam site. Check the time interval at which the images change.
- Still images can be captured at intervals by using a screen capture tool or by using the Print Screen key. Count the number of pedestrians or cars that can be seen in each image.
- Present the findings as a graph.
- Describe the results and suggest reasons for them.

Mind mapping can be done using specialist software. Some interactive whiteboard software allows several layers of links to be created, each nesting as a subset within a larger structure. The organisation chart tool in PowerPoint may provide an alternative tool via which processes and features can be linked. A more basic method is to use a drawing program such as MS Paint in which text can be written and then moved around using the Cut out tool. The same effect can be achieved in a word processor by using editable text boxes. Whichever method is used, it is important to create a strong visual effect that provides a starting point for seeing how the processes work.

Mapping the links

Maps can provide visual clues as to possible links between processes. The links between plate boundaries, earthquakes and volcanic activity provide an obvious example of this. There can also be links between human and physical processes, such as the relationship between rainfall, relief and different types of farming activities. An electronic atlas can be used to show patterns that appear to indicate a visual connection. GIS software has the advantage of being able to select specific layers of data so that the links can be shown more easily.

Proving a link

Visual links on a map are usually not enough to prove that processes are connected. For statistically valid results, one needs to use techniques such as establishing the degree of correlation, either as an index or on a scatter graph with a calculated line of best fit. This can be done quickly using a spreadsheet, as soon as the initial data has been entered. The use of ICT for rapid 'number crunching' can save much of the time involved in lengthy calculations. Even if one does not want to use the automatic tools to work out

Technique tip

Any flash animation on a website can be captured and saved by using a piece of software called Save Flash. Once it has been installed on a computer, an icon is permanently displayed on the Internet Explorer toolbar. To save an animation, right-click on it, select Save with Save Flash, then select and save it from the Save Flash window that appears. The program is available for a free 15-day trial period from the Save Flash website. Note that Save Flash only works with Internet Explorer, not with other browsers such as Firefox. Flash animations can be inserted into a PowerPoint or interactive whiteboard presentation.

Websites

Save Flash
Mix-FX: How to insert SWF files into PowerPoint
Tutorial for inserting flash animations into PowerPoint

Technique tip

Create a flow diagram in MS Paint.

- Draw a set of rectangles using the rectangle drawing tool.
- Write text as labels using the Text tool.
- Cut and drag the text to put it inside the rectangles.
- Move the rectangles and text to suitable positions on the screen.
- Join the rectangles with lines – you can draw in arrow heads using the drawing tool.
- Colour and complete the diagram.

Although this is a basic way of creating a flow diagram, it is quick and easy to do, and the results are visually effective. The finished diagram can then be copied and pasted into another ICT application, or saved as a file for insertion into another application.

Teaching idea

For a topic that you are studying, use a mapping program that can show the distribution of the topic and a range of other variables in separate layers. This could be the ArcVoyager Special Edition, the OS Map program or others.

Look at a map that shows the distribution of the topic, such as the GNP of countries around the world.

- Choose maps to show a range of other themes that might be expected to have some kind of relationship with the topic, e.g., the percentage of people employed in farming or the purchase of newspapers per head.
- Make a visual comparison of the patterns shown by the different maps to see which ones appear to show the greatest degree of similarity. In a GIS program, you can adjust the colours and data range to test for the best match.
- When you have confirmed a match in the patterns, suggest reasons that might explain it. Is there a causal link between the variables? And if so, which variable is creating the other variable?

Teaching idea

Test for correlations between data using the River Form and Channel Analysis program from Geopacks. The program comes with some sample data, but the intention is for students to carry out their own river studies and enter their own data. The program can show statistical correlations between any of the variables that have been entered. The correlation can also be shown on a scatter graph with a best fit line drawn on.

a formula, the calculator from the Accessories part of the Windows bundle of programs is always available. Once an index of correlation has been established, further work can be done to more closely identify what is causing the link.

Modelling change

Answering the 'what if' question in geography is one way in which students can demonstrate their ability to apply their understanding of ideas, skills and knowledge. Asking the question is itself a good starting point. For some questions, the answer may be sought by simply recalculating a set of figures, such as the likely effects on the operating costs of a factory if the price of transport or raw materials were to rise. It is easy to change the data in a spreadsheet and then recalculate the formulae. Another example might be to predict the change in a country's population if the birth or death rate were to change. The complexity of the calculation, whether worked out as a simple or compound interest formula, makes no practical difference to the speed with which the result is obtained. The formula applied to one example can easily be transferred to every other data set, avoiding the need to make a separate calculation for each. Changes to the data table will automatically be shown in graphs.

The 'what if' question can be asked when using some GIS programs such as ArcView. The program has an array of tools that can combine mapping with measuring and making calculations. One could, for example, query the map data to find out how many people would live up to a certain distance from a planned superstore, or within the new noise contours. This is known as buffering. The tools measure the distance from the feature, check this against data in the data table, then make the calculation required.

The power of simulation

Running a simulation is a special form of modelling. In geography, a simulation can be used to show the effects of decisions over time – for example, along a stretch of coastline, designing a city or running a farm. This means a special program has to be written in which the variables are entered and linked to each other. The advantage of using ICT is that the calculations are done automatically. This allows the user to focus on making the decisions and thinking about the consequences of these decisions. Simulations can compress time so that several years' events can be run in minutes.

Hardware modelling

Hardware models run with the help of ICT are less common in geography. An example, however, might be a model for creating waves in a water tank to show how a coastline might be eroded. By using control technology, different patterns of waves could be generated using motors linked to a program or perhaps to sensors. Geography classrooms, however, are not normally set up for this kind of work.

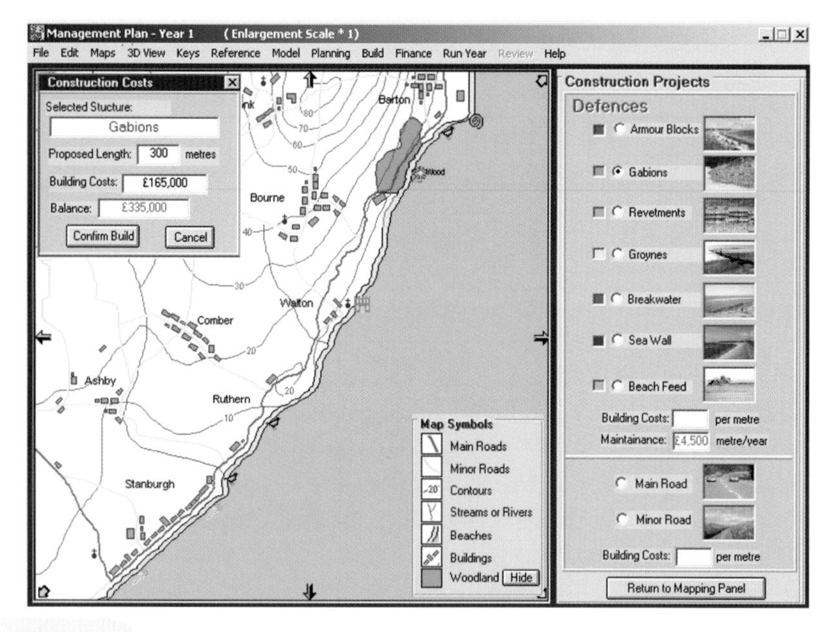

Figure 7.8 *The Coastal Manager program from Geopacks allows students to model how a coastal landscape can be managed in different ways. Variables can be changed to model the effects of decisions.*

Teaching idea
Use Oxfam's 'milking it' simulation to enable students to study the effects of their decisions on running farms in contrasting parts of the world.

Website
Oxfam: Milking it

Teaching idea
The Coastal Manager program from Geopacks enables students to make decisions about defending a stretch of coastline, then study the effects of their decisions as worked out by the program. A decision not to defend one section, for example, can be shown to result in rapid and extensive erosion along that part of the coast. A decision to defend another part with a particular technique can be costed and run as a simulation. Different groups of students could attempt to manage the coastline with specific objectives in mind, such as keeping within a budget or ensuring the defence of some features such as settlements and main roads.

Wider issues in geographical processes

The emphasis in this section has been on ways in which ICT can help students to visualise processes and engage in calculations that help them to understand how the processes work. The idea of links between different processes is also very important in geography. The use of ICT provides opportunities for making these processes more comprehensible, though some caveats are necessary.

Misconceptions of scale and time
If students do not study the 'real thing', it is difficult to prevent them entirely from developing misconceptions about scale, whether in terms of magnitude or time. Even a full-screen image of a major landform can never be enough to really convey a full understanding. A landscape viewed on a computer monitor is enclosed in much the same way as a photo in a book. It also fails to provide the accompanying sounds, smells and moods of the scene. Speeding up a process will enable students to understand how something works, but the very act of speeding it up may also create a misconception of time. Compressing plate movements that have taken place over aeons into the small time-frame of a computer animation can do little to help create a real sense of time. Perhaps this is asking too much.

The accuracy of simulation
Studying the past and present can give valuable clues about the future. ICT is able to help students to test ideas using modelling and simulation programs that have been set up to show the consequences of decisions. A problem,

however, is that the program may not provide any information about the basis on which values have been attached to the data. Writing a program may also create assumptions that are not entirely true, leading students to believe that one could always rely on a computer to produce accurate forecasts of events. A reminder of the accuracy of weather forecasts should be enough to cure them of such a notion. Ideally, the problems associated with writing a program to model a situation will be taught in discrete ICT lessons. If not, it is something that a geography teacher will need to explain.

Making links

Key Stage 3 National Strategy: Literacy and learning in geography

Learning through talk:

- using talk to clarify and present ideas
- active listening to understand
- talking and thinking together.

Understanding the figures

Using a computer to make calculations has the advantage of speed and accuracy. There is, however, the danger that formulae will be used without any real understanding of how they work and what they mean. Perhaps students should always start by working manually on a formula such as a correlation index, so that they can at least gain a basic understanding of how it works. This understanding may also help them spot a wildly inaccurate figure resulting from mistyped data. It is a different question as to why the formula works – one that is probably best left to the realms of statistics. The point, however, is that, once the formula has been worked out by hand on a few occasions, there should be no need to continue to spend time doing it this way.

Working in groups

The usual approach to working with computers is to try to ensure that students are each able to work independently at their own workstation. This, however, may not always be the best way to work with ICT. Running a simulation or game can provide an opportunity for students to use the computer's processing power and visual effects in order to give them more time and more input so that they can discuss what they want to do. This approach may help to reinforce the message that, in spite of the many things that a computer can do well, it is still people who need to make the decisions.

Chapter 8
Fieldwork with ICT

Key questions

- What are the characteristics of high-quality fieldwork?
- How can ICT help to collect and record primary data during a field visit?
- How can mobile technologies be used in fieldwork?
- What are the practical issues in using ICT during fieldwork?
- What issues arise for teaching and learning as a result of using ICT in fieldwork?

ICT applications

- Global Positioning System (GPS)
- Field studies programs (CD-Roms)
- Spreadsheet and database
- Digital camera (still and movie)
- Data logging

Focus on the field

Fieldwork is, or should be, a central part of geographical study. Unfortunately, the number of occasions when most students undertake field studies are few and precious. Researching data and information in the field brings unique dimensions and levels of geographical understanding to both the quality of the data and the research process itself. Photos in books and shown through a data projector are probably best regarded as a necessary substitute for taking the students to real places.

At best, fieldwork is inextricably linked to the wider enquiry process that forms a key part of work in geography. It provides a live context in which data and information can be collected in order to answer questions. The data and information is then presented, processed and analysed for meaning. The part that ICT can play in research, and in presenting data, forms the focus of Chapters 2, 4, 5 and 6. In this chapter, the focus is on how ICT can be used to measure and record real data while students are in the field. The idea of virtual field visits is also briefly considered, though this can never be a substitute for visiting places.

Check it out

Think about the level of importance of fieldwork in your schemes of work.

- Do you make use of your school grounds for fieldwork?
- Does every child get the opportunity to undertake fieldwork at least once every year?
- Are you able to take any of your students on a residential field visit?
- Do you take any of your students on a field visit to another country?

Website

Field Studies Council

Making links

NC Orders for Geography: KS3 PoS

In developing geographical skills, pupils should be taught:

- to select and use appropriate fieldwork techniques [for example, land-use survey, data logging] and instruments [for example, cameras].

In their study of countries and themes, pupils should:

- carry out fieldwork investigations outside the classroom.

Quality in fieldwork

Fieldwork usually involves collecting and recording the raw data and information that can be used to answer a question. This represents one of the stages in carrying out a geographical enquiry. Other aspects of the work can be done back in the classroom, both before and after the visit. So it is mainly the data collection and recording to which quality criteria are applied in this chapter. Some general features of quality in data collection and recording can be identified:

- accuracy
- reliability (linked to quantity)
- variety of types.

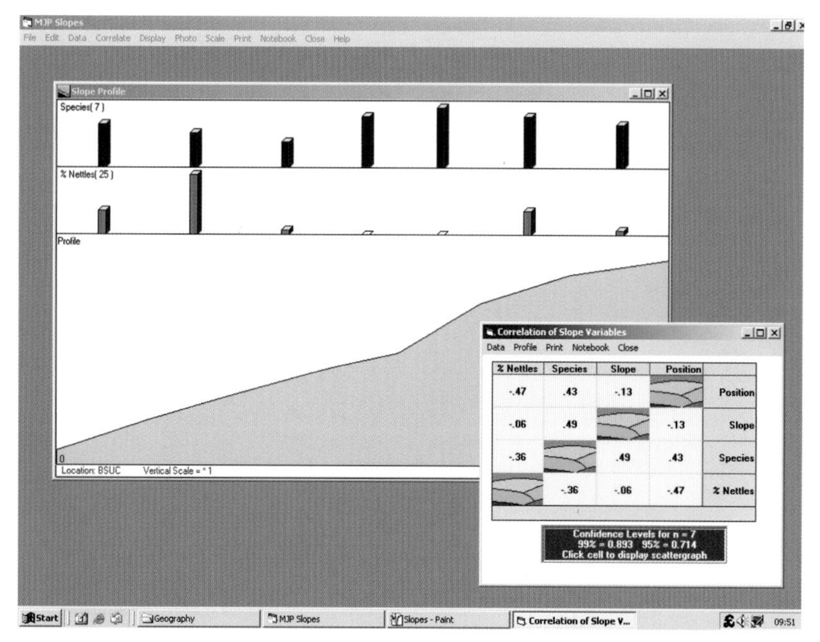

Figure 8.1 *Some programs have been especially written for use with geographical field study work. Although generic software can sometimes be used, a program such as Slopes (illustrated) contains tools and functions that are designed to do the job – in this case, to record, present and statistically process river data.*

© Geopacks 08705 133168

The extent to which ICT can play a part in some or all of these aspects of quality can therefore be explored. Another dimension relates to the extent to which the students are able to carry out their fieldwork independently. This, perhaps, makes the most appropriate starting point.

Independent thinkers

It is probably true to say that some of the highest-quality work that students achieve is often in the area of fieldwork. Although excellent work can be done in groups or as whole-class activities, some of the best is done when individual students are given the opportunity to think independently about a question to research, then design and carry out the work themselves. This often involves carrying out an enquiry into an issue in the local area. Unlike on a school visit, when they are tied to a limited amount of time, they are able to visit and revisit the same sites in their own time. This allows them to build up a comprehensive file of data that so that they can answer their question with greater interest and engagement. This is just one of several compelling arguments why coursework should remain as a major aspect of performance in public examinations such as at GCSE and AS/A2 levels.

Unfortunately, it sometimes seems to be forgotten that to achieve the higher levels in the NC Level Descriptions for Geography, the students should be able to carry out their enquiries with 'growing independence' (Level 7). It is an easy option for teachers to raise their students' levels of performance by doing the work for them! Although this in itself is not an argument that is directly related to the use of ICT, it is one that suggests that time spent in giving students the right ICT tools for their research, whether as hardware or

Making links

QCA Schemes of Work

Being numerate is a product of success in learning mathematics, and pupils' numeracy will benefit from the opportunity to apply their mathematics in geography. Many units give scope to develop mathematical skills, with pupils working with numerical data that relates to real situations. Often pupils will have collected the data themselves. The use of numbers can also add precision to geographical evidence.

Opportunities occur particularly, but not only, when pupils undertake fieldwork, through:

- collecting data, e.g. amount of rainfall, proportion of cloud cover, temperature
- recording data, e.g. using tally sheets or charts to record scores or measurements
- presenting data, e.g. producing tables, block and line graphs, pie diagrams, scatter graphs, flow diagrams
- interpreting data, e.g. comparing patterns, simple correlations, drawing conclusions.

Making links

NC Orders for Geography: Attainment Targets

Level 5
They explain their own views and begin to suggest relevant geographical questions and issues.

Level 6
Drawing on their knowledge and understanding, they suggest relevant geographical questions and issues and appropriate sequences of investigation.

Level 7
With growing independence, they draw on their knowledge and understanding to identify geographical questions and issues and establish their own sequence of investigation.

Making links

NC Orders: Thinking Skills

Fieldwork can involve every aspect of thinking skills. In this list, some have been identified as having special relevance for fieldwork.

Information-processing skills enable pupils to:
- locate, collect and recall relevant information
- interpret information to show they understand relevant concepts and ideas
- analyse information e.g. sort, classify, sequence, compare and contrast
- understand relationships e.g. part/whole relationships.

Enquiry skills enable pupils to:
- ask relevant questions
- pose and define problems
- plan what to do and how to research
- predict outcomes, test conclusions and improve ideas.

Reasoning skills enable pupils to:
- draw inferences and make deductions
- make judgements and decisions informed by reasons or evidence.

Creative thinking skills enable pupils to:
- generate and extend ideas
- suggest possible hypotheses
- be imaginative in their thinking.

Evaluation skills enable pupils to:
- evaluate information they are given (or find out for themselves)
- judge the value of what they read, hear and do (or see)
- develop criteria for judging the value of their own and others' work or ideas.

Check it out

Think about how you ensure that there is progression in your enquiry and field-study work during key stage 3.

- How and when do you introduce the idea that students should be asking their own questions for an enquiry?
- To achieve the higher levels, do you insist that students set their own enquiry questions for a field visit, or does the whole class work on the same question that you have set? Does this differ between year groups?
- During key stage 3, do any students have the opportunity to ask their own questions and carry out their own field study research?

software, is likely to be time well spent. The time restrictions in a geography classroom do nothing to help raise the quality of students' work in the subject. They are often capable of better, but are not always given the expectations or opportunities.

Accurate data

Accurate data can be difficult to obtain during geographical fieldwork. In physical geography, measurement of natural features and processes is seldom easy. This is sometimes because of safety and access. It can also be because the instruments used to measure the features are relatively unsophisticated. Scientific method and aims are the ideal, but work in the field is rather different from work in a laboratory. For example, counting the number of plant species in a given area can usually only be done with a degree of error that is difficult to quantify. Even measuring the dimensions of a sample of beach sediment is problematic, whether for its longest and shortest axes or for its index of roundness. The smallest pieces of sediment may be too small to measure and the biggest may be too big to move.

Measurements in field conditions, usually without proper scientific equipment, often produce results that although usable, would hardly meet strict scientific criteria for accuracy. The equipment used is often home made from tin cans, plastic bottles and even dog biscuits (for stream flow). It is hard to justify the cost of proper equipment when so little fieldwork is done, and home-made equipment is sometimes just as effective. Yet for geographical studies that need to demonstrate statistical techniques to meet exam-board criteria, it can be far easier to collect data about physical than about human geography – hence the understandable popularity of river and beach studies.

Some features of human geography are relatively easy to measure, such as land use and traffic flows. It becomes more difficult to obtain accurate data when recording subjective data, such as people's reactions to the quality of a landscape, even when using an index to do so.

In spite of these problems, students should be expected to collect data that is as accurate as can reasonably be achieved. Where accurate recording equipment is available, it should set the standard for what can be expected. There is, for example, no reason why an estimate of temperature or wind speed should be acceptable when simple and accurate measuring equipment is available. It is the responsibility of geography teachers to make sure that it is available so that standards can be set to the highest levels.

Reliable data

Although individual measurements may be accurate, the data cannot be said to be reliable if the sample is too small. Statistical techniques are available to provide indices of reliability, the general principle being that more data is likely to be more reliable than less. One can calculate the minimum and a maximum number of measurements needed in order to give results that have different degrees of reliability. Collecting large amounts of data can be extremely boring and also uncomfortable in poor weather conditions, though working in groups that share data can help to overcome this problem. Another problem is that the data is often collected only on the day of the field visit. The window of time in which it is collected may be unrepresentative of the situation at other times. A limited quantity of data on selected occasions may prove nothing.

In school fieldwork, the convention is that the limitations of data collection are usually accepted. What is more important is that the students demonstrate their awareness of the limitations by presenting their conclusions with suitable caveats and recommendations for how the study could be improved. Perhaps for higher-quality work, the standard required should give more credit for collecting an appropriate amount of data, in addition to the ability to comment on the method of collecting it and on its reliability.

Varied data

Not all fieldwork data is collected as figures. Field sketches, for example, are a traditional way of recording the landscape. Field sketches can also record more detailed landscape features, such as details on buildings or small-scale features on a rocky wave-cut platform. The main purpose of a field sketch is to provide a visual record of the scene – especially of those aspects that are relevant to the study. A field sketch can also serve as a format on which to make notes and add labels about what has been seen.

A high-quality record is one that shows the features in a way that is easily recognisable and that has labels to the key features in appropriate places. A hand-drawn sketch is certainly one way to do this. Some teachers prefer a field sketch to have mud on it to demonstrate its authenticity! Nowadays, students are able to make a visual record by taking a photograph with a digital camera. They can then annotate it in a word processor or drawing program. This raises questions about whether drawing a field sketch is still an essential geographical skill. Drawing field sketches was an essential skill in the days when explorers travelled the world on sailing ships without any kind of camera. There are still some reasons why students should be able to draw a field sketch, but teachers and students need to be clear about what these reasons are. If they have more to do with history than quality, then perhaps the students' fieldwork will be better served by capturing the scene in a more effective and efficient manner.

Fieldwork also usually involves some form of mapping. Some field studies involve accurately drawing an original map, especially where the scale of the study makes it difficult to use a published map. Mapping also involves making a record of land use. The features of high-quality mapping are considered in Chapter 4, so are not repeated here.

Check it out

Think about the emphasis that you place on the accuracy and statistical reliability of raw data for fieldwork enquiries in GCSE coursework.

- Do you award marks for accuracy and reliability?
- Do you make use of any statistical techniques that will enable students to test the reliability of their results, and do you know if this kind of work is done in maths lessons?
- Does the weight of your marking go towards the method used rather than the reliability of the results?
- What is the weighting of marks given to the student's ability to provide a critique of their research methods and findings?

There is no definitive set of answers to these questions, but rather they are intended to raise some issues about how much emphasis should be placed on ensuring that field-study methods produce valid results.

Using ICT for fieldwork

ICT can play a part in fieldwork during all phases of the work. The focus in this section, however, is on how digital resources can be used in the field to measure and record raw data and information. Some equipment is available for professional surveying work such as laser technology for measuring distances. This kind of equipment is generally beyond the budgets of school geography departments. ICT equipment that is available for field-study work in schools includes the following:

- Global Positioning System (GPS)
- data recording on a spreadsheet or database
- data logging
- digital cameras (still and movie)
- mobile phone technologies.

Global Positioning System

The Global Positioning System (GPS) tells you where you are. GPS information is transmitted from satellites in permanent orbit around the Earth. It is received on a small handheld monitor that gives data for height and position with an accuracy that is within a few metres. For position, it can show either grid references or latitude and longitude. If geography is to lay claim to 'real world' relevance, it should be part of every geography department's work to make sure that their students gain some experience of GPS technology.

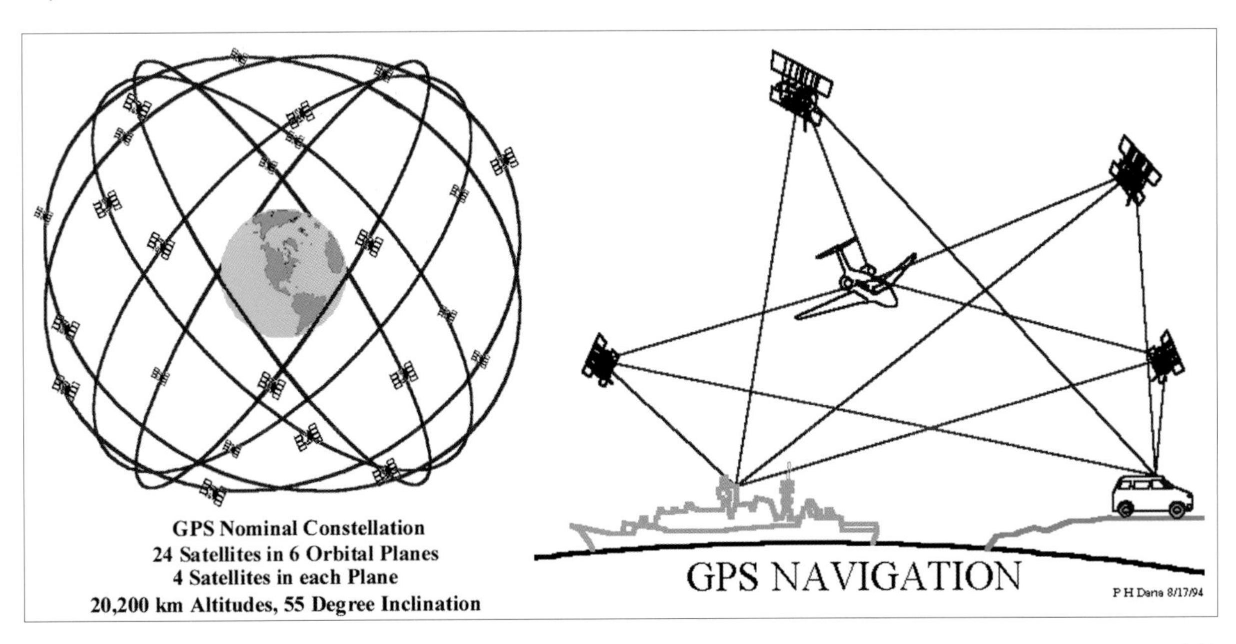

Figure 8.2 *These diagrams show how GPS works to give accurate location and height information. This system has become an essential part of mapping and navigation, and as such should be part of every student's geographical education.*

© Peter H Dana, The Geographers' Craft Project

Teaching idea

Use GPS to create a trail for students to follow. This will mean buying a set of GPS receivers or making use of equipment at a field-study centre.

Websites
Geocaching
University of Colorado: The Global Positioning System
NavCity
GPS equipment

Use during fieldwork is an obvious application of GPS technology. The only question is the age of the students for whom this would be appropriate. The equipment is as easy to use as a mobile phone, so perhaps the only age-related requirement is that students should also understand something about direction, distance, height and how to work out a grid reference. This is within the capabilities of students at key stage 2 and certainly at key stage 3.

Data can be recorded at points along a trail, a transect or at other sample points, and the position of the data can be recorded at the same time. Knowledge of a six-figure grid reference system is no longer enough. Students now need to know how to work with a ten-figure grid. GPS-located data can then be fed seamlessly into a GIS program, bringing data recording and mapping together.

Data recording

Fieldwork data can be recorded on a spreadsheet or in a database, though using ICT hardware in the field can create problems. Taking a full-sized laptop computer into the field is not a good idea. Apart from their size and weight, they are unlikely to be robust enough to withstand either the elements or the users under field conditions. But then neither is paper, though paper is cheaper. Handheld computers and other handheld hardware can provide alternatives that are practical and effective. The data can then be transferred to a desktop or laptop PC, either back at a field-study centre or at school.

Data logging

Data logging usually involves specialist measuring equipment such as that used for recording light, heat or sound. There are sensors and peripherals that can be connected to a computer. In geography, digital data loggers can give an instant record of soil measurements such as pH values. This can replace the more tactile experience of putting soil, fluid and powder into a glass file, waiting until the liquid changes colour and matching the colour against a chart.

Weather stations are another kind of data logging equipment. A fixed weather station on a building in the school grounds can both give a current reading and take a record over a longer period of time. Although it is stretching a point to say that this is fieldwork, it is a means of using ICT to collect primary raw data. It also provides a means of recording the data in a standard way, without being subject to the vagaries of individual readers. A portable system is also possible. This could be used to study microclimates around the school grounds or elsewhere.

Teaching idea

Set up a school weather station using automatic data-logging equipment. Compare your school's data with data from other school weather sites.

Websites

Hardenhuish High School

MetNetUK

Meteorological data site for schools

Shipston High School, Warwickshire

Weather stations worldwide

Digital images

The traditional way to make a visual record of a scene during fieldwork is to draw a field sketch. Although cameras are not new, and students have used photo prints as part of field studies for a long time, the digital camera has brought new opportunities for this kind of work. Photos can be integrated into text as illustrations, with or without annotation. They may also play an important part in a field study that investigates landscape change. Simple photo editing can show what a scene might look like, for example, if something is either added to, or removed, from the landscape. Questions about whether digital photos can replace drawing field sketches are discussed in Chapter 6.

Figure 8.3 *The Hardenhuish School Weather Station is run by the school's geography department. The results are put on the school's website.*

Hardenhuish School Weather station

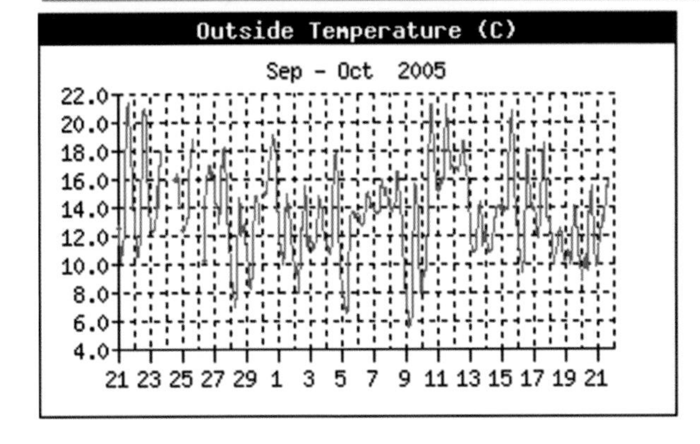

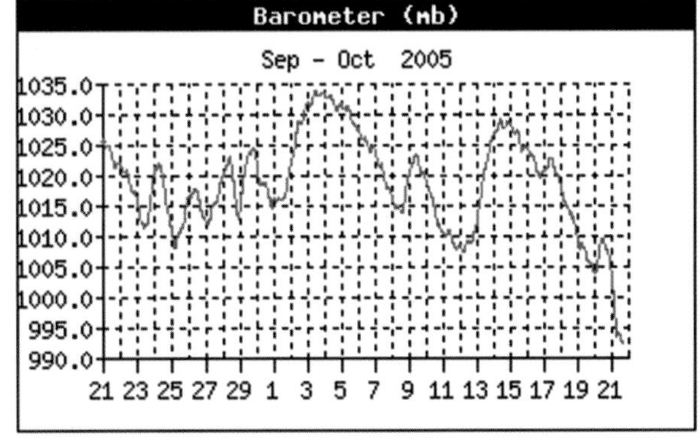

The DigiMemo device from Unimatic is an example of how ICT can create a bridge between traditional skills and digital technologies. The device is a handheld sketch pad that uses a pen to create a digital image. This can be downloaded into a drawing program for further editing, or copied and pasted into a word-processed document. The device was designed for taking notes that can be converted to text and for drawing simple sketches. Both facilities could be used during fieldwork.

Check it out

Look at the Unimatic website to see further details of the DigiMemo. Think about whether this or a similar device could be used in geography. In particular, think about any particular pupils who might benefit from a device such as this.

Website

Unimatic: DigiMemo

Some processes that can be seen during a field study would benefit from being recorded as a movie – for example, to show wave action on a beach or a human process such as pedestrian flows in a shopping centre. Digital movies have the added dimension of sound. A field visit to study a planning issue in relation to an airport expansion would be better served by the inclusion of sound, rather than relying solely on text and photos. Digital movie hardware is still relatively expensive, though as sales continue to rise, prices are likely to fall. The divide between a digital camera that takes still images and one that takes movie images is one that is rapidly being reduced. Some cameras can do both.

Figure 8.4 *The DigiMemo is a drawing pad that can produce digital images from hand-drawn sketches.*

Teaching idea

The students could investigate the most suitable site for a scenic beauty spot.

- Begin by working out what criteria they think would be required for a suitable site.
- Visit several sites, and at each site take a series of digital photos so as to create panorama images for a 360-degree view of the surrounding area.
- Compare the images to see which one meets the criteria best.

There are some examples of panorama websites in Chapter 6.

Mobile technologies

There is a new generation of mobile technologies that offers potential for fieldwork in geography. Links can be made to satellites for both receiving and transmitting data and information. Some mobile phones have built-in cameras that can record a scene. Others have a more complex range of facilities, including internet access, data recording and the ability to write text. These offer opportunities for instant access to background data and information, not only before and after fieldwork, but also during it.

One recent experiment using mobile technologies was a project to provide a spoken commentary of historic events while visitors walked around part of a city (Queen's Square in Bristol). The visitors carried a backpack with a satellite receiver, and heard a commentary being spoken through headphones. The idea is similar to using headphones to listen to a recorded commentary while

Teaching idea

Use the Coast project on the BBC website to find a stretch of coastline you want to study. This site uses maps, photos and audio commentaries that can be downloaded. Use these resources to carry out an enquiry into the ways in which people use the coast and the types of land-use conflict that can crop up. Compare different stretches of coastline that have similar physical features to see whether the land is used in similar ways.

Website

BBC: Coast
BBC: Coast: Audio Walks

Teaching idea

The students can collect multi-media resources for a place for which there is a local planning issue to resolve. This might be to investigate whether a village should have a bypass, or whether a base station should be built, or some similar issue.

The resources can include:

- photos
- movies
- raw data as figures
- sound
- text for descriptions and understanding.

Use a multi-media authoring program such as Opus, or web authoring software, to create a virtual field visit that could be used by anyone who wanted to find out about the issue. The resources should be linked with buttons or hyperlinks to allow the resources to be visited in any order.

Check it out

Think about the occasions when you help your students to develop the skills of field sketching.

- Do you have a set of criteria that can be applied to field sketching?
- Do you have performance indicators that show how progression can be achieved in field sketching?
- Do you think that there is a level beyond which progression in field sketching effectively stops? If you do, at about what age should that be reached?
- How might you mark a hand-drawn field sketch in comparison with one taken with a digital camera and annotated in a word processor or image-processing program?

walking around a museum. The same technology could be applied to work in geography. For example, a field study enquiry could be created at a coastal location, during which students could walk to different sites to collect information. At each site they could listen to a commentary that asks questions, gives information and suggests some data that could be collected. Although this may appear rather fanciful, the technology for it already exists and is already in use. The BBC's Coast project, based on a TV series that was broadcast in 2005, makes use of mobile technologies to provide commentaries on coastal walks that people can listen to via their mobile phones. A map of the walk could either be printed out from a website, or seen on a mobile phone with internet access. This technology is simply waiting for someone to use it for fieldwork in geography. A national network covering a variety of fieldwork sites would make an interesting long-term project for any company or organisation with an interest in helping students to explore and understand their environment.

Erosion of the Holderness coast

Holderness is a lowland region of England that lies between the chalk hills of the Wolds and the North Sea. It is part of the East Riding of Yorkshire.

The region is composed almost entirely of glacial, alluvial and lacustrine deposits, little of which is much more than 12 000 years old. These soft, recent deposits sit on a platform of chalk which slopes away gently to the east.

Follow the links on the left to find out more about the geography of Holderness and the processes of coastal erosion.

Click on the map to the right for pictures of the sea defences

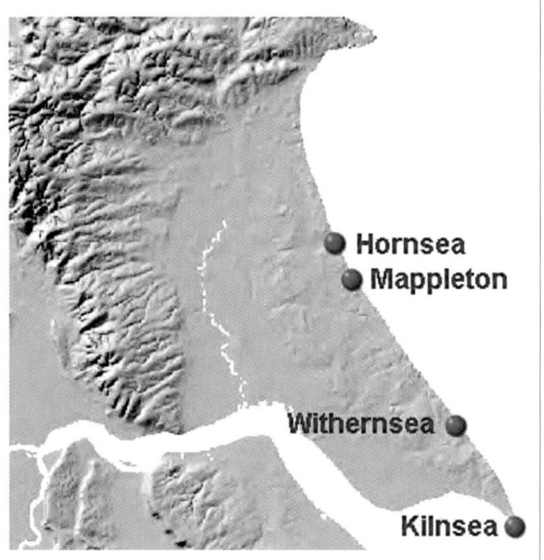

Figure 8.5 *This image shows part of a virtual field course (VFC) devised by the University of Hull geography department. The study provides data and information about coastal processes along the Holderness coastline. This resource could be used in addition to a field visit, or serve as a resource for an enquiry based on secondary research.*

© University of Hull Geography Department

Virtual field visits

A virtual field visit, also called a VFC (virtual field course), involves providing students with a range of resources for locations that they cannot visit, or even for locations that they do visit. Virtual field visits are usually found on websites, though some can be purchased on CD-Rom. Their content varies from little more than a set of slides with notes to fully worked resources with simulated field-visit activities.

At best, VFCs are a way of accessing data and information about places that cannot be studied at first hand. The place may be one that is similar in some ways to a place to be studied in the field, or one that is simply impractical to visit. This is not to decry the value of resources that allow students to carry out enquiries in 'virtual' places. A good virtual visit can provide students with an educational experience that can stimulate thought and engage them in an interactive learning process. A virtual pre-visit can also be a useful way of raising questions about an area so that students can become more independent in creating their own enquiries. It is one way of avoiding the need for every student in a class to visit a site with the same enquiry title, thereby denying them the opportunity to achieve the higher levels in National Curriculum or exam board assessment.

Check it out

'A virtual field trip is like a virtual pint of beer' – Chris Durbin.

- What do you see to be the value of virtual field visits?
- Do VTCs have any benefits for achieving inclusion?
- Should every field visit be backed up by a VTC as a preliminary resource?
- What is the best format in which to produce a VTC?

Teaching idea

There are examples of virtual visits on websites. Some of these could be used if accompanied by a worksheet, preferably based around a set of questions.

Websites

Teachers Resource Exchange
University of Hull Department of Geography: Erosion of the Holderness coast
Jurassic Coast
Volcano world: Mount St Helens VR Tour
SwissEduc: Stromboli on line
Biz/ed: Virtual Worlds
Virtual visits include:

- five field trips to Zambia, a virtual visit
- visit to a balloon factory in Cameroon
- managing a farm.

CTI: Virtual Worlds and Fieldtrips
Pearson Publishing Group: Virtual Visits
CD-Roms of River Esk and Whitby
NW Grid for Learning: VTC studies
Virtual field visits to:

- the dune coastline of Sefton
- a long profile of the River Dane
- zones of urban settlement
- the hydrological cycle
- floods at Wildboarclough
- pollution along the River Alt.

Strolling
A virtual visit to London
Go North!
A polar expedition

Wider issues in ICT for fieldwork

The use of digital technologies in the field raises a set of technical, economic, academic and pedagogical issues. These issues are hard to untangle. The more complex the technology, the greater the cost. More complex technology may also require extra time teaching students how to use it, though it is usually the tools and not the technology behind it that need to be taught. Using more costly equipment becomes problematic in the field when there is a risk of damage. However, some key issues are worth discussing.

A 'real world' subject

One argument for using digital technologies as part of fieldwork relates to geography's claim to be a 'real world' subject – a phrase that is often interpreted as meaning a work-related or vocational subject. To make this aspiration a reality, it is logical that the most appropriate equipment should be used. Even though there will still be economic constraints, the question then becomes one of economic priorities. 'Real world' geography may not be cheap. Perhaps the growing value given to the vocational dimension – for example, at GCSE and post-16 levels – will provide the additional incentive needed to justify the cost of good field-study equipment. Perhaps there are some links that should be made to areas of employment such as civil engineering.

The time dimension

It takes time to teach students the skills and techniques to make use of digital technologies for fieldwork. Of course, time spent on something new will have to be at the expense of something old. Some digital technologies are likely to take the same or even less time to learn than older methods – taking pH readings for example. But where extra time is needed, it may be worth asking whether the arguments over 'real world' applications of the subject are sufficiently important to justify the time. Another consideration is whether any extra time can be justified by gains in the quality and quantity of the data that can be collected by the use of ICT. If not, then perhaps the process of enquiry and data collection is more important than the results.

The field study experience

A field study can sometimes be a memorable 'get wet' and 'get dirty' experience, especially when studying aspects of physical geography. Even human geography in the field can have moments when the wider experience helps to engage students in the work. It is worth considering whether the use of digital equipment might take something away from this experience. The effort needed to draw a field sketch in wet and windy conditions cannot be replaced by the ease of taking a digital photo. If measurement by lasers becomes a reality in schools, students will miss the memorable experience of wading across a river to measure it – though perhaps the increasing emphasis on safety will stop this kind of work even before the technology becomes available. There is also an element of engagement when students can build their own equipment to measure features in the field. There must, however, come a point when we must face up to the disadvantages of maintaining what is little more than an amateurish approach to the subject.

The cost equation

Geography is a minority subject. This has implications for the economies of scale that operate on the purchase of resources whose use is limited to only a few students on only a few occasions in each year. ICT equipment can be expensive, though experience has already shown that the cost of digital equipment usually falls. Sharing costs with another department may be an option, but few other departments engage in fieldwork, and when they do, they may need different equipment.

One solution that already exists is to make use of residential field centres. The fact that fieldwork takes place every day surely justifies the cost of ICT resources. Some field-study centres have already embraced ICT, though many have not, preferring to spend as much time in the field as possible, rather than teaching students how to use ICT software and equipment, either in the field or in a classroom. Some field-study centres do not seem to appreciate the requirement from exam boards to incorporate ICT in field studies. The result is that students may end up carrying out the ICT component of their coursework back in the classroom, using little more than a word processor, except perhaps for some basic use of a spreadsheet or a digital camera. There may be a case for more field-study centres using ICT as part of their work.

The basic premise

The premise on which this chapter is based is that the use of digital resources is in itself likely to result in more accurate, more reliable and more varied data. The extent to which this is true is open to question. One could, for example, question whether the measurement of a river's velocity is likely to be more accurate and reliable using a digitally operated flow meter compared with timing how quickly a dog biscuit or an orange can move when dropped in the river. The same question can be asked about taking temperature readings with a data logger compared with reading figures from a handheld thermometer. In some cases, the accuracy and reliability of the data will only be as good as the person operating the equipment, whether digital or not. In other cases, it may be best to leave the measurement and recording to instruments that operate automatically and are more sensitive to what they are measuring. One may be tempted to assume that digital equipment is inevitably better, but the part played by those operating it should never be ignored.

The VFC experience

Virtual field visits create some issues in teaching and learning that need to be addressed. One problem is that everything on the 'visit' is controlled by the person who created it. Another is that there can by definition be no sense of actually being there or of making real measurements. There may even be a temptation to regard a VFC as an alternative experience for students as opposed to a complementary one. This can be because of the inherent risks involved in undertaking field visits, or perhaps because some students are not able or allowed to undertake the visit. In spite of the solution that virtual field visits may seem to offer, one should never be tempted to replace a live field study with a virtual one. Inclusion should mean that everyone can take part in the real and not just the virtual visit.

Integrating the work

Although the focus for this chapter has been on ICT in the field, fieldwork on its own is likely to form only one part of a geographical enquiry. ICT can help to provide secondary information about a topic and a place. It is also the case that during the planning stage some account must be taken of how the data will be collected, recorded, processed and presented. This can mean thinking about the structure and layout of a spreadsheet or database. It can involve taking account of how features should be mapped, especially if GIS is to be used. Although the type and format of the tools should not drive the research, it is inevitable that their effects should at least be appreciated.

Check it out

NESTA Futurelab is an ICT think-tank that aims to make creative use of ICT for teaching and learning, taking ideas that have not been tried before and developing them to prototype stage. It may be worth checking out their website to see what they are doing for geography. If you have a good idea, contact them and see if they will make it a reality.

Website

NESTA Futurelab

Chapter 9 Only the start

Key questions

- What common themes link the use of ICT for different purposes in geography?
- Why is it important to define a clear set of criteria for high-quality work in geography?
- How can the use of ICT play a key part in raising standards of teaching and learning in geography when set against the current criteria for success?
- What opportunities does ICT offer for redefining the content, standards and success criteria in geography?
- What needs to be done to integrate the use of ICT fully into all aspects of work in geography?
- What is the role of the teacher in teaching and learning with ICT?

Focus on themes

The structure of this book has meant that a number of themes relating to the teaching and learning of geography have recurred in more than one chapter. The aim of this concluding chapter is to bring these themes together in order to provide some final ideas about the directions in which the use of ICT in the teaching and learning in geography might lead us. There are some areas where some caution is needed, such as the move towards online assessment. There are other ideas that should be fully embraced, such as the opportunity for students to have a degree of choice in the content of their studies.

These ideas, however, need to be set against the current background of the content and assessment criteria for geography as determined by the NC Orders for Geography and exam boards at GCSE and post-16 levels. These criteria have served to act, no doubt unintentionally, as a dead hand on how the subject might have progressed. It can be difficult to see beyond these statements of subject content and assessment criteria, especially in the context of the current inspection regime, which has created a climate in which experimenting with new ideas and new technologies has carried a high, and in many cases unacceptable, level of risk. Perhaps this problem has simply been the result of unfortunate timing. The success criteria for teaching geography were mostly written down before there was any real understanding of what ICT could offer to work in geography. There is, however, no reason why the body of professional geographers, including teachers, should not be able to create their own definitions of quality in their subject.

Common themes

The themes that have been presented in the different chapters can be listed as follows:

- defining quality in geography
- creating benchmark standards for quality
- gaps between students and schools in their ICT resources and capability
- changes to the content and assessment criteria for work in geography
- providing students with opportunities for choice
- the value of a multi-media approach for work in geography
- issues in the assessment of ICT work in geography
- technical, cost and access issues.

In search of quality

It has been argued throughout this book that the issue of raising achievement levels can only be addressed fully if one defines 'achievement' in terms that lie beyond the NC Orders for Geography and exam board assessment criteria. At best, one can argue that the NC Orders and exam board criteria do not deliberately hinder the teaching and learning of high-quality geography. One can, however, also argue that the success criteria are so poorly defined that there is insufficient direction as to what good-quality geography should look like, and therefore little explicit incentive or direction to teach it.

Perhaps the basis for ideas about real quality in the subject should be sought elsewhere. This should be in a shared understanding among the community of professional educators who work with the subject, i.e. the teachers and others who work most closely with geography in schools. It follows that the assessment of geography should then have an appropriate emphasis on these more sharply defined definitions of quality. This is not to deny the need to involve others from outside the geographical community in shaping the subject's content, ideas and skills. It does, however, put the key decisions about how it should be taught, and the quality criteria against which it should be assessed, within the hands of the community of geography educators.

Benchmark standards

In each chapter, it has been argued that the use of ICT has the potential to raise the benchmark against which standards of high-quality work can be assessed. It would be to go too far to say that ICT holds the key to raising every aspect of performance, but there are some aspects where, for sheer quality, there can be very little contest. This raises the question as to whether the use of ICT by some should be allowed to set the standards for all. The position argued here is that it should.

This position, of course, opens arguments about fairness between students and between schools, i.e. between those that have access to ICT resources and those that have not. If raising standards is to mean anything, then it is

Check it out

BECTA, in its summary of research into the use of ICT in geography, lists a number of findings (given below) in relation to students and teachers.

- How convinced are you that your students' learning and your own teaching would benefit in these ways?
- Which of these benefits do you feel would make the greatest impact on your students' achievement in geography?

BECTA: Benefits for pupils

- Geographical Information Systems (GIS) simplify many geographical concepts and present large amounts of non-sequentially related data in simple and readily accessible formats, allowing pupils to concentrate on interpreting and analysing data.
- Using GIS software enhances spatial awareness and decision-making skills.
- Using simulations and modelling tools can lead to enhanced understanding of geographical topics such as erosion and agriculture.
- ICT enables higher-level thinking skills, especially for pupils using GIS.
- Using digital photography in a classroom mapping activity helps develop recall, reflection and self-assessment skills.
- Interactive ICT such as e-mail enables the exploration of a sense of place, through communicating with people as well as through pictorial features.
- Using e-mails alongside postcards to make comparisons of places helps pupils to gain a better appreciation of other cultures.

BECTA: Benefits for teachers

- Using GIS can significantly enhance geography teaching and learning environments.
- Digital photography allows teachers to record pupils' work undertaken on field trips, and other learning outcomes not readily recorded in traditional ways.
- ICT enables teachers to engage and motivate pupils about geographical concepts to a greater degree.
- Using GIS software to produce and manipulate maps at a range of scales can save lesson time and give better quality results.
- The internet increases access to authentic geographical data and information sources.
- GIS software can enable teachers to focus more closely on teaching geographical skills, in addition to developing a sense of location and place.

Website

BECTA: What the Research Says

Check it out

Use the *National Curriculum in Action* website to look at samples of students' work and how it can be assessed against the level descriptions.

- Do you agree with the comments made about the work and the levels that have been suggested?
- For work that has included the use of ICT, what levels of ICT have been achieved?
- In what ways do you think that the use of ICT has affected the quality of the work?
- Are there any ways in which the quality of the work could be raised even further by the use of ICT?

Website

National Curriculum in Action: Geography: ICT Learning

This site gives 26 samples of students' work at key stage 3 with assessment indicated for levels.

hard to argue that one should accept a lower standard than is possible by some, and that lack of resources can be used as justification for not reaching those standards. This is an uncompromising position to hold, but it is one that is put forward in order to drag some teaching and learning of geography into the present digital century. Besides, the idea of lack of resources as a reason for poor standards has never been accepted as valid, whether this applies to the number of books in a school, the number of students in a class or the qualifications and skills of the teacher. In this respect, ICT is just another resource.

Mind the ICT gap

One key theme has been that, although ICT has been used in schools for several decades, the NC Orders for Geography and exam board specifications do not appear to reflect this fact. This is rather odd, since the NC Orders for ICT were introduced at the same time as the NC Orders for Geography, and both have subsequently been modified at the same time. There are some references to the use of ICT in the Orders for Geography and in exam board specifications, but these tend to be provided as examples of what *could* be done, rather than what *must* be done. The orders do not, of course, indicate how the teaching should be done. The QCA Schemes of Work give guidance on this, though these are non-statutory, and at best should be regarded as suggestions and examples of good practice. Moreover, there seems to be no expectation that the required levels of ICT at different key stages should be linked to the way in which these levels are applied in different subjects, including geography. A similar position could be said to exist for work in numeracy. Perhaps the Secondary (KS3) Strategy ICTAC plan will do something to address this omission.

The idea of 'joined-up' thinking across different subjects has never been strong in British schools. The development of the National Strategies is doing something to change this situation. The idea of literacy and numeracy across the curriculum has begun to take root. However, until recently the same cannot be said for the Strategy for ICT, where during the initial phases, in apparent denial of previous experience, ICT was turned back into itself as a discrete subject. This is unfortunate, because as with literacy and numeracy, the use of ICT is a key skill that is in need of both context and content. Geography is one subject that can provide both. This is another aspect of ICT work that the ICTAC documents have begun to address.

Old and new

Time in the school curriculum is not elastic. So if something new is brought in, something old usually has to be left out, or at least downgraded. It can be argued that the use of ICT saves time, though the time may need to be spent in teaching students how to use it, or more importantly to appreciate the choices it offers and how it can best be used. Perhaps this is another example of where stronger links need to be forged between geography and

ICT. In previous chapters, questions have been raised about whether students should still be expected to draw graphs by hand, at least beyond the stage at which little further progression can be achieved. The same argument has been put for some other traditional geographical skills. But far from downgrading the importance of displaying data as graphs, the use of ICT now opens opportunities, and indeed the requirement, to develop a far wider and deeper understanding of the characteristics of the graphs that students are asked to produce. This is a case where a time-consuming traditional skill can be replaced by one that achieves a better end result, combined with a much higher level of understanding.

Opportunities for choice

The use of ICT provides opportunities for students to become more independent, both in *how* they learn and in *what* they learn. Although there is still a need to create a framework of concepts to be studied, the use of ICT through the web and other ICT applications can provide students with a much greater element of choice. Choice helps to create ownership, engagement, and hopefully also the motivation to find out more. The traditional textbook has served to restrict choice and, even worse in many cases, has been used as a single source of geographical knowledge and understanding. The question is not about whether student choice is possible for those with access to ICT resources. It clearly is possible. The question is one of whether teachers are willing and able to provide the kind of guidance that will enable their students to take advantage of those choices. Giving tight guidance ensures that every student conforms to narrow assessment criteria. Opening up the choice with more flexible guidance runs a risk of lower achievement as it is currently defined. But this is a risk worth taking for the sake of greater involvement by the students and for the sake of moving the subject on in other ways.

The multi-media approach

The use of ICT enables every aspect of geography to be taught using a multi-media approach. The educational theory behind using this approach is sound. The theory is backed up by what teachers experience with their students every day in the classroom. Catering for learners who are predominantly visual, auditory or kinaesthetic in their approach can be greatly facilitated by the use of ICT, though, as has been discussed earlier, the kinaesthetic aspect is perhaps more open to argument.

But even for work in the subject itself, using a multi-media approach brings real benefits. The study of a place, for example, is made infinitely richer by being able not only to read about it, but also to see and hear the sights and sounds of the place. The ideal kinaesthetic experience would be to visit the place, but because this is usually unrealistic, the virtual visit brought through the medium of ICT will have to suffice.

Check it out

The ideas of Howard Gardner about multiple intelligence can provide an academic framework against which to plan for using ICT in geography. Think about how these ideas can be applied to using ICT for work in geography. Examples are provided below for each aspect of multiple intelligence. What are your experiences and what do you think?

- linguistic – the use of words through web research, writing with a word processor and word-games programs
- mathematical and logical – data handling with a spreadsheet or database
- visual and spatial – using photos and maps in GIS, presentations, image processing and mind mapping
- musical – including digital sound in presentations, web authoring or other multi-media authoring software
- interpersonal – web research, e-communications with others, and discussion during a decision-making activity or simulation
- intrapersonal – opportunities for independent work, e.g. through web research
- kinaesthetic – using data-logging equipment or simulating activities on a screen, e.g. by drag and drop activities
- naturalistic – access to digital images
- existential (environmental) – web research about environmental issues.

Check it out

How would you respond if you discovered that one of your students had used a 'homework help' website? Which of these three responses below would be appropriate?

- Give credit for the student's level of motivation and ability to research.
- Say it is acceptable, but that the source should have been acknowledged.
- Give it a lower mark because it had not been done independently.

Or is there a different response you would prefer to make?

Website
BBC: SOS Teacher

Assessment issues

The assessment of ICT work can create real problems for a variety of reasons, including the need for different assessment criteria. There are also more practical issues to do with knowing who did the work. These are issues to which too little attention has been given, and for which there are too few solutions. The problem of downloading work from websites has already been identified as a problem at university level, but it is also a growing problem for work in schools. Some websites have been set up in order to give assistance to students, for example, by providing 'model' answers. It is unfortunately only a short step from giving assistance to providing an opportunity for unfair practice. At the moment, perhaps, the greater issue is the extent to which the boundary between formative and summative assessments is being blurred by teachers in an attempt to be seen to be raising standards. This is an issue for the teaching profession to resolve. If we don't, then others will do it for us.

Technical and cost issues

There have been barriers to progress throughout the introduction and development of ICT in schools. It has often been left to the school's 'ICT maverick' to persevere through these problems and to forge a way ahead. An early problem was the lack of processing capacity in the first generation of school computers. There was also a problem of projection because of the poor quality of LDC panels. Currently, the cost of upgrading classrooms with network capability, and the high cost of interactive whiteboards, are two of the problems preventing ICT resources from being introduced at an even faster rate than at present. The high cost of replacing a bulb in a data projector, and high levels of theft of ICT equipment, are other problems that often crop up. Experience has shown that all of these problems can eventually be solved, as long as the need to resolve them can be demonstrated.

One problem has persisted for which it is hard to see any immediate solution – the problem of printing students' work so that the teacher can assess it. The cost of printer ink, especially for work in colour, is prohibitive. The slow speed of printing usually means that, unless there is a printer attached to each computer in a computer suite, it is difficult for all the students' work to be printed and handed in at the end of a lesson or even later. This is quite apart from the rather temperamental behaviour to which printers appear to be prone, leading to paper jams and other problems. Although the students' work can be sent to a shared area or sent by e-mail, this creates a range of other problems for the teacher. Teachers often have neither the access to ICT nor the personal working space in schools for this to be done. For the moment this is a problem in search of a solution, though this rather basic issue seems to have been given a much lower priority than other more technologically interesting and high-profile developments in ICT.

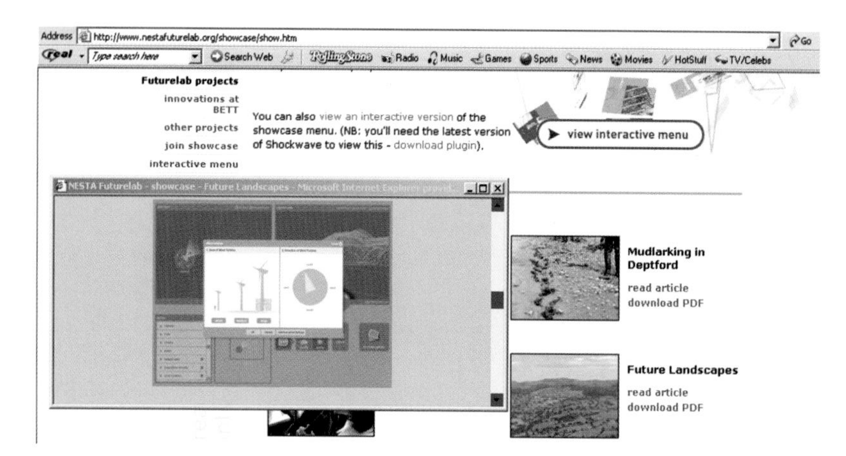

Figure 9.1 *NESTA Futurelab is an organisation funded by the New Opportunities Fund (NOF) to explore ideas about how ICT can be used in education. They bring together software and experts in different fields of ICT to create prototype products, some of which may be developed in the future.*

© NESTA Futurelab

Forward planning

In the early days of ICT, some teachers appeared to take the view, that like so many other educational initiatives, it would 'go away' or at least confine itself to a few devotees. There is still some resistance to using ICT, especially in subjects where a computer is seen as a threat to the traditional ways of doing things. In geography, however, the overwhelming reception of ICT by teachers has been positive. Geography teachers in many schools have led the way in developing new and exciting ways to use ICT in their classrooms. For those who have not, it has mostly been because of inadequate training, poor resources and a lack of confidence to use it. Sometimes, it has been felt that it would bring no measurable benefits to achievement. At worst, there has been a fear that it could adversely affect GCSE and AS/A2 level grades. It is, however, a technology that is here to stay, so the only approach is to understand it, take control of it and take advantage of it.

Planning for ICT in geography

Planning for the use of ICT involves thinking about the many ways that ICT can play a part in the geography curriculum at every level. It involves taking a long-term approach, taking students on with the skills they have learnt in their primary schools and developing them throughout their secondary-school years. It will be important to establish clear links to their work in discrete ICT lessons, and perhaps also to ICT work in other subjects. Schemes of work should not leave the use of ICT to chance or to the individual preferences of each teacher. The students should have an entitlement to ICT that goes beyond these random factors, especially where issues of the quality of geography are concerned.

The ICTAC guidance advises that work in geography should make use of skills in ICT that have been taught in a previous year. This is certainly one way to make sure that the geography teacher does not have to teach the ICT skills to work in geography, even though there is something illogical in introducing a

Check it out

The ICTAC guidance includes the statements below about linking work in ICT to work in geography.

- What are the implications of this guidance for the ICT work that you do in geography?
- Are there any ways in which you would want to adapt this model?

ICTAC: ICT in Geography
It is expected that:

- year 6 ICT capability will support year 7 work in geography
- year 7 ICT capability will support later year 7 and year 8 work in geography.
- year 8 ICT capability will support later year 8 and year 9 work in geography.
- year 9 ICT capability will support both later year 9 work in geography and GCSE work.

Check it out

Carry out a review of how you make use of ICT, focusing on the practical issues that affect the extent to which you use it.

- Identify what you think could be some of the barriers to greater use.
- How could some of these barriers be removed?

Website
Getting the most out of a computer room: Managing ICT

context for the skills a year after they have been taught. It is also a relationship that is rather more complex and that will need more detailed planning. Work in ICT, for example, is not going to teach students how to use GIS software, though it will teach students how to use a database and how to use vector-based drawing tools. Bringing these ICT skills together is still likely to be the preserve of the geography teacher.

The need to train

Teachers need to develop the knowledge and skills to make effective use of ICT, both when working in a classroom with a single computer linked to an interactive whiteboard, and with students who are working independently in a computer suite. One of the greatest problems in getting started is not being able to make regular use of ICT. Without regular use, it is too easy to forget how to do something or, worse still, never find out. ICT is not a technology that one can use effectively by dipping into it occasionally. It only becomes effective when it becomes an integral and constant part of how teachers teach and how learners learn.

The vision thing

There needs to be a clear vision as to where the geography department wants its work with ICT to be in several years. A few years is about as far as one can predict in the fast-changing world of ICT. As time has progressed, there seem to be fewer 'dead-end' technologies, and therefore less fear of heading off in costly and ultimately unproductive directions. More of these 'dead-end' technologies, however, are bound to appear, and they will be hard to identify as such at the time. One problem is that the hardware and systems in a school are seldom, if ever, under the control of a geography department. The influence of a geography department is usually limited to the software and perhaps also to some peripherals. Geography teachers need to stay alert to changes in the technologies so that they can at least make an input to decision making when necessary.

The vision needs to take account of how to transform the classroom and the teaching strategies. It also needs to take account of how the students of the future will learn best, recognising that they will become more skilled in using ICT, including mobile technologies, in a wide range of contexts. Some of these technologies and contexts may be outside the classroom, though they may still have applications for work in schools.

Learning from others

One of the greatest potential benefits of the growth in digital technologies has been the opportunity for teachers to communicate with each other and learn from what others have done. This is especially useful when there are limited INSET opportunities for teachers to have direct contact. There is already a wealth of experience in the use of ICT in geography and in other subjects. The list of departmental websites cited in Chapter 1 gives evidence of this. Digital

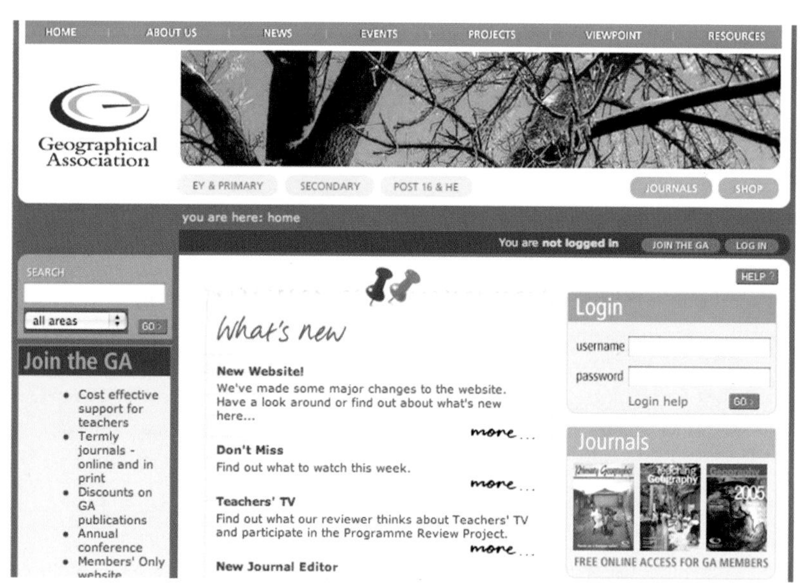

Figure 9.2 *The Geographical Association's website gives access to professional guidance and information about developments in geography, including the use of ICT.*

resources can be downloaded, then used 'off the shelf' or adapted as necessary. Teachers can learn from each other about how to set up their own intranet sites, and students can share data and information. There is no need for every teacher to be an 'ICT pioneer'. Within the Geographical Association, the ICT working group provides ongoing information and support through articles in *Teaching Geography* and on its website. Sharing expertise in the use of ICT is important since it seems that no single person can claim expertise in every aspect of it.

As part of this process, it is important to work out what you need to know and what is best left to others. Most teachers, for example, do not need to know how to create a website in HTML code or how to write a program. Some tasks relating to ICT have become too technical and specialist, and are therefore best left to those who have these specialist skills and the time to use them. No teacher should feel that the technology in ICT is a barrier to using it. For the teacher, the emphasis should be on the information and the communications. This is not to say that nothing new needs to be learnt, for example, in making use of different ICT applications. This, however, should be a matter of time, training and practice, not of technical difficulty.

Online exams

The prospect of online exams seems to be moving ever closer. Some exam boards are already undertaking trials in public examinations that involve students working online. This avoids the need to employ as many markers. In some subjects, it may take out some of the elements of subjectivity that can be involved in awarding marks. For work in geography, there are some aspects of the work for which this kind of assessment may be suitable. ICT, for example, is good at assessments that involve clear 'right' or 'wrong'

Check it out

You can find samples of ICT work in geography at these websites. Think about the value of sharing work in this way and make a decision to send in some of your own work.

Websites

BECTA: Exemplifying ICT Use in Geography
Includes National Parks, development data, population data, multi-cultural Birmingham

Teacher Resource Exchange
An extensive range of samples provided by teachers

answers. There may even be some other kinds of work that should be assessed online, such as a student's ability to use a GIS.

There are, however, some real dangers in moving too far or exclusively in this direction. It has been argued throughout this book that there are some things that ICT is good at doing, but there are also some things that it is not good at doing. ICT is not, for example, good at assessing a reasoned explanation of a geographical process or students' understanding of their own or other people's viewpoints. These are not the kinds of things that can be assessed by multiple-choice questions. Attempts to mark a student's explanation by picking up key words in their text seem to be highly problematic. Any attempts to use unsuitable online methods to assess work in geography will need to be resisted. The dangers of having the content and teaching methods driven by the style of assessment are all too obvious.

The role of the teacher

The idea that computer-based learning can in some way replace the role of the teacher has sometimes been voiced. Although integrated learning systems have been used for several years in some subjects, it is hard to see how the role of the geography teacher can be anything other than enhanced by the use of ICT. Instead of working from a limited range of textbooks, the teacher now needs to become adept at teaching with, and managing, a much wider range of multi-media resources. These need to be selected and used with care so that the essential geography is always at the forefront. The geography teacher also has a responsibility to ensure that the students' work is synchronised with work in ICT, as well as in other areas of key skills. The sheer amount of digital resources to which students have access means that even greater guidance for students is needed, both in research techniques and in how to select appropriate materials. The issue of defining standards in the subject is also one that the geography teacher needs to resolve, clarifying the standards expected, and in some instances taking the definitions beyond what is currently stated. Besides, although the technology of ICT can bring many benefits, it is still the individual skills and personal enthusiasm of the teacher that will generate the interest and the motivation in wanting to learn.

Geography at a crossroads

Geography has entered a period of slow decline in its popularity as a GCSE subject. It is in danger of losing ground at key stage 3 as the National Curriculum framework is made more flexible to cater for the needs of the growing number of specialist schools. Yet at best, geography can remain one of the most dynamic and relevant subjects in the curriculum. ICT has the potential to help students to achieve higher standards in the subject. It also has the potential not only to do existing things better, but also to move the subject into some new areas of skills and content. These may create a new relationship between

Check it out

Look on the Geographical Association's website to find out about the ICT working group. Use the contact address to find out what the working group can do to help you develop the ICT capabilities in your department.

Websites

Geographical Association: ICT Working Group

Check it out

Read these comments from the QCA in relation to e-assessment:

- We know that learners are motivated by e-assessments and that increasingly computers play a prominent part in their studies and lives. Learners are not threatened by assessments delivered through the computer and they are not disadvantaged by them. Indeed, in some cases they can demonstrate higher levels of attainment when working on a computer.
- It is clear that access to computers improves learners' performance. E-assessment can provide timely feedback to inform future teaching and learning, and 'when ready' assessments give learners greater ownership of their learning. With e-assessments it is possible to test areas of knowledge, skills and understanding that would be impossible using pen-and-paper-based testing. What could be the implications of these statements for your teaching?

Check it out

Look at the QCA website to see its vision for e-assessment. Is this a vision with which you would agree?

The strategic objective for the QCA, for awarding bodies and for learning providers is that by 2009:

- all new qualifications must include an option for on-screen assessment
- all awarding bodies should be set up to accept and assess e-portfolios
- all existing GCSE, AS and A2 examinations should be available on-screen
- the first on-demand assessments should be starting to be introduced
- at least 10 new qualifications, specifically designed for electronic delivery and assessment, should be developed, accredited and live.

Website

QCA

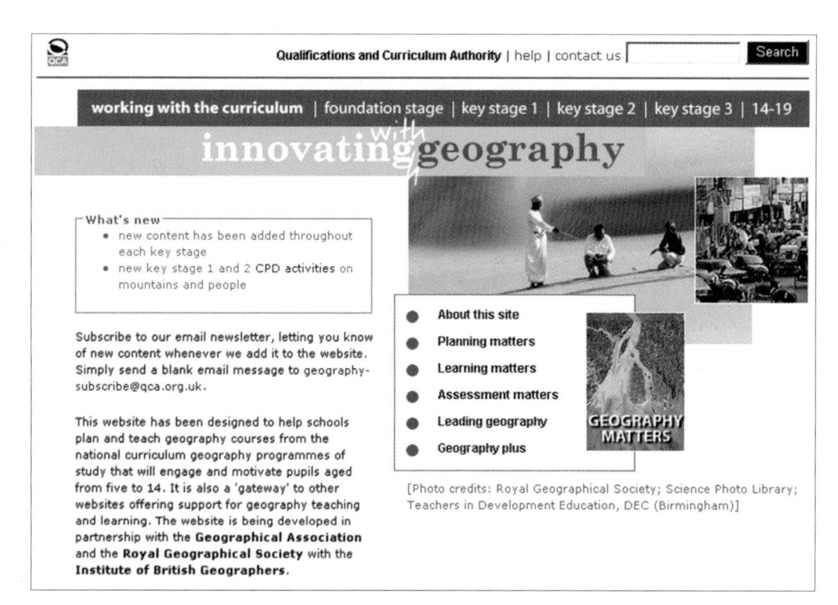

Figure 9.3 *The QCA's* Innovating with Geography *website is a source of practical guidance through the many documents that have been developed in recent years. This guidance includes classroom ideas from practising teachers. (www.qca.org.uk/geography/ innovating/)*

the academic and the vocational aspects of the subject. Perhaps there are also some new areas of conceptual understanding that will follow. In an increasingly digital world, it would be surprising if this were not the case.

At the moment, there seems to be a distinct possibility that the extensive use of ICT in some schools and the dearth of ICT in others could lead to a splitting of the subject into geographies that are very different. One would be ICT-rich in both how it is taught and what is taught. The other would remain traditional, keeping the old skills and only using ICT to fulfil minimal requirements. If this is the scenario that will develop, it will be interesting to see how students and others respond. It is clear that teachers of geography need to think carefully about the direction they want to take so that they can control of, rather than be controlled by, a digital revolution that can only become more influential.